ELECTRICAL
SCIENCE

ELECTRICAL SCIENCE

BOOK 1
RESISTIVE AND DIODE NETWORKS

NORMAN BALABANIAN
PROFESSOR OF ELECTRICAL ENGINEERING
SYRACUSE UNIVERSITY

WILBUR R. LePAGE
PROFESSOR AND CHAIRMAN OF ELECTRICAL ENGINEERING
SYRACUSE UNIVERSITY

McGRAW-HILL BOOK COMPANY
NEW YORK/ST. LOUIS/SAN FRANCISCO
DÜSSELDORF/LONDON/MEXICO
PANAMA/SYDNEY/TORONTO

Electrical Science

Library of Congress Catalog Card Number 75-116658

03543

1234567890 MAMM 79876543210

This book was set in Caledonia by B. Handelman Associates, Inc.,
and printed on permanent paper and bound by The Maple Press Company.
The designer was J. Paul Kirouac;
the drawings were done by B. Handelman Associates, Inc.
The editors were B. G. Dandison, Jr., Michael Elia, and Margaret LaMacchia.
Adam Jacobs supervised production.

PREFACE

This book is a programmed text, designed to provide instruction in selected areas from the general subject "electrical science." The level is appropriate for beginning students, requiring as prerequisites the rudiments of differential and integral calculus; and preferably some prior introduction to electrical phenomena, as given in elementary physics. The prerequisites are defined rather explicitly by a set of test questions on mathematics and physics, which appears at the beginning. Although electrical science is not synonomous with network theory, the topics selected for this book are network-oriented and are confined to those situations in which energy storage is absent.

There are many styles of programmed texts, all of which have in common the careful attention by the author to identification of objectives, organization of sequences, avoidance of ambiguities, and choice of responses. The style of this particular text was designed to be consistent with these objectives, while providing a format which is convenient for subsequent use as a reference book. We have paid a great deal of attention to clarifying meanings and removing uncertainties in wording. Consequently, we believe that responses made by a student will tend accurately to reflect his knowledge. The process of preparation, which has extended over a period of seven years, included trial use by more than 1,000 students from seven institutions besides Syracuse University.

The text is organized into six units. The word "unit" refers to a cohesive set of closely interrelated topics and was chosen in preference to "chapter" in order to enhance the differentiation between this style of text and a conventional one. There is not necessarily the close relationship among units that is normally expected among the chapters of a conventional book.

We believe that programmed texts are particularly appropriate for teaching at the beginning levels of analytical subjects, because the pertinent skills must be learned to a high level of proficiency, to the point where appropriate responses become "automatic." It must be realized that a programmed text has certain distinctive features which must be appreciated by teacher and student. If it is viewed and used as an ordinary text, much of its effectiveness will be lost. Accordingly, separate specific recommendations are made for teachers and students.

TO THE TEACHER

One of the inevitable questions a teacher may ask about a programmed text is how to decide what role it should play in the educational program. Is it the primary text in a conventional course? Is it supplementary to another text? Is it only for self-study? Our thoughts concerning this particular text are as follows.

Each unit has certain specific objectives. For attainment of these objectives the programmed text can be viewed as sufficient. Summary outlines of the objectives of the various units are given below, but a more complete appraisal of the objectives can be obtained from a detailed inspection of the text itself. It is not possible for a teacher to evaluate this book in the conventional way; it is necessary to sample the experience the student will have. That experience is as important as the subject content.

It will be observed that the objectives are defined operationally, by statements of what a student should be able to *do*. These objectives are among those which must be met, almost completely, early in a student's career, and which can be attained by the student only with a high degree of personal involvement. It is therefore recommended that the teacher rely on the programmed material for the attainment of these objectives, avoiding the introduction of parallel lectures or of reading material which might dilute the student's effort. Of course, individual help to students on points which are difficult for them will be necessary. For attainment of the objectives of the programmed material, the teacher should assume that completion of the text by a student is sufficient. Accordingly, the teacher's role should be one of encouragement and help. Carefully chosen supplementary exercises may be appropriate, but it is important that they blend in with the programmed material. The text units include sets of exercise problems which are judged to be sufficient for most students, insofar as the attainment of the specific objectives of the units is concerned.

The objectives of a *course* are likely to be much broader than the objectives of this programmed text. It is the teacher's responsibility to decide what these additional objectives are, and to provide means to attain them through classroom instruction and perhaps additional text material and exercise problems. However, to the greatest extent possible, the teaching format should be designed so that the attainment of additional objectives does not interfere with the student's continuity of thought in the programmed material. One way to accomplish this is by placing the programmed text learning in time sequence with experiences pertinent to the other objectives, although this may not necessarily be the preferred method in all situations.

SUMMARY OF OBJECTIVES
Units 1, 2, and 3 are concerned with those fundamental concepts which are the basic "language" of the circuit viewpoint of electrical phenomena. After completing these units a student should be able to:

1   Relate current to charge and voltage to work.

2   Identify junctions and loops in networks.

3   Write Kirchhoff's current and voltage equations, while insisting on identification of reference orientations for all currents and voltages.

4   Identify ideal source and resistive elements by their current-voltage relationships and as standardized circuit symbols; write Ohm's law.

5   Obtain equivalents of physical generators employing an ideal source (voltage or current) and a resistive element.

6   Relate power to energy and to voltage and current.

After completing Unit 4, the student should be able to do the following:

1   When given a network of moderate complexity (up to four junctions or ten branches), containing specified resistors and voltage and/or current sources which can be time-vary-

ing, find the voltages and/or currents at any branch of the network, or the power dissipated in a resistor, or supplied by a source.

2 When given the structure of a network of complexity similar to the above, in which certain resistance and/or source values are unspecified, determine the values of one or more components so that the network will meet a specified design objective. Such design objective might be to maximize the power delivered to a load, to balance a bridge, to provide a fixed attenuation of a voltage or current, to measure voltages or currents in given ranges, or to supply a given power at a given voltage.

3 Do each of the above by any of the following methods:
   (a) Alternate application of Kirchhoff's laws and Ohm's law
   (b) Use of a Thevenin equivalent or a Norton equivalent
   (c) Use of voltage-divider and/or current-divider relationships
   (d) Systematic application of Kirchhoff's laws and Ohm's law in a specific manner, leading to a set of simultaneous algebraic equations called node equations, whose variables are voltages only
   (e) Systematic application of Kirchhoff's laws and Ohm's law in an alternate specific manner, leading to a set of simultaneous algebraic equations called loop equations, whose variables are currents only

Unit 5 is concerned with the theory of network graphs. After completing this unit, the student should be able to do the following:

1 If a network of electrical components is given:
   (a) Draw a linear graph representing the network.
   (b) Distinguish between a planar and nonplanar graph.
   (c) Identify trees, twigs, cotrees, links, cut-sets and loops.
   (d) Write the incidence matrix.
   (e) Write the loop matrix of the fundamental loops for any tree.
   (f) Write the cut-set matrix of the fundamental cut-sets for any tree.

2 If an incidence matrix is given, either complete or reduced, draw the corresponding graph.

3 For any graph, be able to specify: the number of twigs in a tree, the number of links in a cotree, the number of fundamental cut-sets, and the number of fundamental loops.

After completing Unit 6, which deals with diodes and diode circuits, a student should be able to do the following:

1 Given a network containing an ideal diode, one or more resistors, and one or more constant (dc) sources, find the state of the diode and determine the values of all voltages and currents in the network.

2 Repeat the above for networks having two ideal diodes.

3 For networks having components as described above, when there is also an input signal (voltage or current) varying with time, determine the ranges of the input for which the diodes are in each possible state. From this, calculate a curve of an output voltage or current versus the input, and determine the waveform of the output.

4 Repeat (3) when the diodes are assumed to be replaced by a piecewise-linear model.

5 Given a network containing a diode described by its actual nonlinear current-voltage graph, with one or more resistors and one or more constant (dc) sources find the diode voltage or current by a graphical procedure that includes the "load line."

6 For a network as in (5), determine the permissible values of an unspecified resistor or source, in order that the power dissipated by the diode shall not exceed its rated value.

TO THE STUDENT

The style in which this book is written is based on the assumption that learning takes place only when there is active participation of the learner. It has been prepared according to principles of learning that have emerged from empirical results in the psychological laboratories and in the classrooms.

The material is so arranged that you are frequently asked to supply *responses*. These responses may consist of filling in a blank, selecting one out of two or more alternatives, making a numerical calculation, deriving a formula, or drawing a diagram. Confirmation of the answer is supplied on the side of the page.

The question and answer form of the material may give the impression that it is a test; *it is not*. It is designed to help you learn. The questions are not designed to trip you up—you are expected to answer almost all of them correctly. Sometimes the answers may seem so obvious that you may doubt the merits of such trivial things. Fill in the answer anyway; it won't take much time and it may not be as simple as you think. The very act of writing answers will help you to learn. Do not look at an answer until you have committed yourself to your own answer. *This is important*.

It is very important that you write out any steps required, and for that purpose you should provide yourself with a notebook. In this way, you can preserve what you do for possible later reference, rather than lose it on a piece of scrap paper.

The material is organized in the following form. Each major division of the book is a *unit*. Each unit is subdivided into *sections* numbered consecutively within the unit. Sometimes, there is material of a basic nature to which it is necessary to refer repeatedly. Such material has been included in separate sections which are labeled *Reference Section*. They require no responses. You should read them once or twice when they are first encountered, and refer to them again as often as needed. There is another type of section requiring no response. This is labeled *Remark*. These sections provide related comments that round out a phase of the subject, but which are not directly relevant to subsequent responses.

When a relatively lengthy word statement is required as an answer, you are unlikely to use the same combination of words as given in the confirmation. This is recognized by writing OES after the statement in the confirmation, as an abbreviation for "Or Equivalent Statement." When you see OES, you should examine your answer to make sure it includes all of the elements of the statement in the confirmation.

Certain sections consist largely of review problems. After the statement of each problem, try to obtain a solution without further directions. If you cannot, and you need help, a solution is outlined below the problem. You can use this outline to get hints; but go only as far as you need to before you can complete the problem yourself. For ease in finding the confirmation of the answers without reading the entire outlined solution, there is an arrow like this ←—— opposite each answer.

In some instances, a particular topic is not of fundamental importance but extends a previously developed concept. It will not hurt the subsequent material if this topic is skipped, and so it is labeled "optional."

The mksc (meter-kilogram-second-coulomb) system of units is used in this text. When a quantity is first introduced, its unit of measure is given. Subsequently, in numerical problems, units of measure are sometimes omitted. The appropriate mksc unit is implied. Thus, on a diagram where a voltage might be labeled 50 without specifying its unit of measure, it means 50 volts. If it were meant to be 50 millivolts, the unit of measure would be specified.

To obtain the maximum benefit from this text, stick to the following tactics:

1 *Write out each answer.*

2 *Do not look at the given answer before you have written your own answer.*

3 *Do not make snap judgments when choosing among alternatives, but think through the consequences of each choice.*

ACKNOWLEDGMENTS

A large number of individuals and organizations have helped in the development of this book in various ways, and we wish to express our gratitude to them. We acknowledge our debt to the Bureau of Research, U.S. Office of Education, for awarding us a contract to develop educational materials, during which development the early drafts of some of this material were prepared. We also wish to thank the Ford Foundation, the Esso Foundation, and five other companies (IBM, Xerox, GE, AT &T, Western Electric), who helped to finance the Programmed Learning Project of the American Society for Engineering Education. Finally, we wish to acknowledge a debt to the Programmed Institution Center of IBM at Poughkeepsie, N.Y., for providing the opportunity to develop other programmed materials that indirectly helped this book.

Many individuals have contributed in bringing this book to its present state. Among these are the numerous students who gave us their views and comments. We wish to thank all our colleagues who taught the course from early drafts of the program and who gave us many useful comments; special thanks go to Messrs. Gerald Kirwin and Donald Reynolds. We further wish to acknowledge a specific debt to Dr. Gerald Kirwin who helped write the first draft of Unit 6. In addition, we acknowledge the help of Profs. E. J. Wagner and Charles H. Roth, Jr. of the University of Texas and Prof. Henry Ablin of the University of Nebraska, who used the material with their students and supplied us with many ideas for revision.

We owe a special debt to Dr. A. A. Root who supplied invaluable detailed editorial help throughout all phases of the development of this material and with whom we have had innumerable discussions on programmed instruction.

NORMAN BALABANIAN
WILBUR R. LePAGE

CONTENTS

Prerequisites

Certain mathematics and physics prerequisites are necessary in order to go through this book successfully. To see if you have these necessary prerequisites, a brief test is given here. If you have difficulty answering any of the items, you should obtain a book dealing with the corresponding topic and study it before proceeding. Complete the test before checking your answers at the end.

1   Metric units.
   (a)   A kilometer is _____ meters.
   (b)   A microjoule of energy is _____ joules.
   (c)   How many milliliters are there in 1 liter? _____
   (d)   One meter contains how many centimeters? _____
   (e)   Write the number of units represented by the following notation:
      (i)   A c newton is 10^{-2} newtons.
      (ii) A μ meter is _____ meters.
      (iii) An m coulomb is _____ coulombs.
      (iv) A k anything is _____ anythings.

2   Find the roots of the following equations:
   (a) $x^2 + 5x + 6 = 0$
   (b) $2t^2 + 4t + 4 = 0$

3   Solve the following sets of equations for the unknowns:

    (a) $3x - 2y = 5$

         $-x + 4y = 0$

    (b) $6v_1 - 5v_2 = 0$

         $-5v_1 + 18v_2 - 3v_3 = 77t$

              $-v_2 + 3v_3 = 0$

4   (a)   Write the equation of the straight line shown in the graph below.

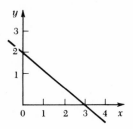

    (b)   A straight line passes through the points (1,1) and (3,2). Write the equation of the line.

    (c)   A straight line of slope -2 in the vi plane intersects the horizontal axis at $v = 10$. Write the equation of the line.

5   (a)   Expand each of the trigonometric functions below:

        (i) $\cos{(\alpha + \beta)}$

       (ii) $\sin{(x - y)}$

    (b)   For each of the functions below, write another expression (or identity) that does not include the square of any function:

        (i) $\cos^2 x$

       (ii) $\sin 2\alpha$

     (iii) $\sin^2 \omega t$

    (c)   Write the following in terms of trigonometric functions of the sum and/or difference of two angles:

        (i) $\sin x \cos y$

       (ii) $\cos \alpha \cos \beta$

     (iii) $\sin \omega t \sin \theta$

6   Find the value of x at which the quantity y has a maximum value, and find this maximum value for each of the following functions:

(a) $y = x^3 + 6x^2 + 10$

(b) $y = \dfrac{2x}{x^2 + 4}$

7   Find the approximate value of the derivative of the curve, shown in the graph below, at the point $x = 2$.

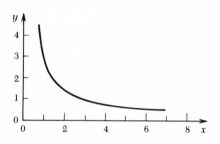

8   On the axes beside the given graph, sketch a curve which at each point gives the derivative of the original graph.

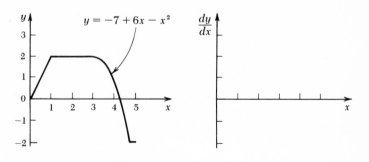

9   Evaluate the following integrals:

(a) $\displaystyle\int_1^t (3x^2 + 4x + 5)\, dx$

(b) $\displaystyle\int_0^\pi 10 \cos^2 \theta \, d\theta$

10 On the axes beside the given graph sketch a curve which
    at each point gives the integral of the original graph up
    to that point. Do you expect your curve to have dis-
    continuities (jumps)?

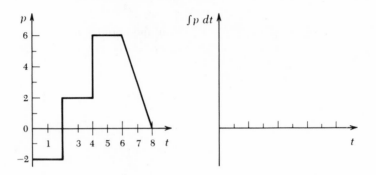

ANSWERS TO TEST

1 (a) 1,000   (b) 10^{-6} (c) 1,000   (d) 100
   (e) (ii) 10^{-6} (μ = micro)   (iii) 10^{-3} (m = milli)
        (iv) 10^3 (k = kilo)

2 (a) $x = -2, -3$ (b) $t = 1 \pm j1$ $(j = \sqrt{-1})$

3 (a) $x = 2, y = \frac{1}{2}$ (b) $v_1 = 5t, v_2 = 6t, v_3 = 2t$

4 (a) $y = -\frac{2}{3}x + 2$ (b) $y = \frac{1}{2}x + \frac{1}{2}$ (c) $i = -2v + 20$

5 (a)   (i) $\cos(\alpha + \beta) = \cos\alpha\cos\beta - \sin\alpha\sin\beta$
         (ii) $\sin(x - y) = \sin x\cos y - \cos x\sin y$

   (b)   (i) $\cos^2 x = \dfrac{1 + \cos 2x}{2}$ (ii) $\sin 2\alpha = 2\sin\alpha\cos\alpha$

         (iii) $\sin^2\omega t = \dfrac{1 - \cos 2\omega t}{2}$

   (c)   (i) $\sin x\cos y = \frac{1}{2}[\sin(x + y) + \sin(x - y)]$
         (ii) $\cos\alpha\cos\beta = \frac{1}{2}[\cos(\alpha + \beta) + \cos(\alpha - \beta)]$
         (iii) $\sin\omega t\sin\theta = \frac{1}{2}[\cos(\omega t - \theta) - \cos(\omega t + \theta)]$

6 (a) $y = 42$(max at $x = -4$)
   (b) $y = \frac{1}{2}$(max at $x = 2$)

7   Slope of tangent at $x = 2 \approx -0.7$

8

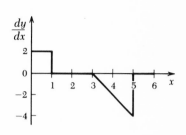

9   (a) $x^3 + 2x^2 + 5x \Big|_1^t = t^3 + 2t^2 + 5t - 8$

       (b) 5π

10

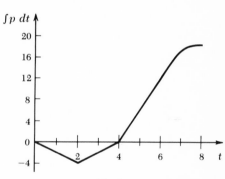

No discontinuity

Current and Kirchhoff's Current Law

1 INTRODUCTION

The notion of *electric charge* has grown as a consequence of man's observations of a large number of phenomena. These range from observations of gross phenomena, such as lightning and electric sparks jumping between objects that have been rubbed, to sophisticated observations, such as the paths of charged particles in a cloud chamber. The idea of electric charge is part of the atomic theory of matter and is a major building block in the structure developed by physicists to describe nature.

It has been known for more than two centuries that objects, which we can now describe as being electrically charged, may exert forces of attraction or repulsion on each other from a distance, such forces being related to the amount of charge.

Quantitative laws have been formulated which describe and allow us to predict the behavior of charged bodies. Application of these laws by engineers has led to the development and design of a host of useful accomplishments—from electrically powered industrial and home machinery to telephonic communication; from radio and television to devices for medical diagnosis and treatment; from the guidance and control of space vehicles to laser-beam communications and the microwave broiling of hamburgers.

In this unit, we shall be concerned with the motion of charges flowing along a path, thus constituting an electric current. We shall relate the sense, or orientation, of the current to the sign of the charge. We shall also discuss the way in which currents flowing along a number of paths, but coming together at one point, are related to each other.

2   CURRENT (REFERENCE SECTION)

The smallest known amount of charge is that of an electron. However, this is so small compared to the amount of charge involved in practical situations, that it is not commonly chosen as a unit of measure. In the meter-kilogram-second (mks) system of measurements, the unit of charge is called the *coulomb*, named after a Frenchman who first gave a quantitative relationship for the force of attraction or repulsion of one electric charge on another. One coulomb equals 6.25×10^{18} times the magnitude of the charge of an electron; or stated alternately, an electronic charge equals 1.6×10^{-19} coulomb. The charge on an electron is negative.

In many situations, electric charges can move when subjected to forces. In metallic conductors, the moving charges are electrons, and hence negative. On the other hand, the plasma in a neon lamp contains both moving electrons and positive ions. Thus, current can be due to the motion of either positive or negative charge, or both.

In developing a definition of current, suppose there is a cloud of positive charges, in which all charges are moving along parallel paths, as in the illustration below.

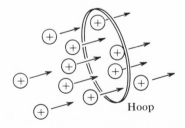

Hoop

Furthermore, imagine a hoop placed in such a way that charges pass through the hoop as time progresses; and also imagine you are sitting on the hoop and counting positive charges as they pass through the hoop. (This is essentially the same as sitting by the side of the road and counting cars as they go by.)

The *average* current equals $\Delta q/\Delta t$, where Δq is the amount of charge that passes by in time interval Δt; in this expression, charge and time are, respectively, in coulombs and seconds. The physical dimension of current is *coulombs per second*, but current has its own unit, the *ampere* (abbreviated amp). As an example, if charges are counted for half an hour and found to total 3,600 coul, then since half an hour is 1,800 sec, the average current will be

$$\text{Average current} = \frac{3,600}{1,800} = 2 \text{ amp}$$

An average taken over such a long interval as this will not tell in detail what happens during that interval. For example, it might be that during the first 5 min 1,200 coul would pass; during the next 10 min no charge would pass; during the next 5 min charge would actually go the other way in the amount of 900 coul; and during the last 10 min 3,300 coul would pass. This would give

$$\Delta q = 1,200 + 0 - 900 + 3,300 = 3,600$$

in the half-hour interval and, consequently, an average current of 2 amp, as computed above.

A larger amount of information can be obtained for this half-hour interval by counting for smaller intervals of time; say, 15 min in this example. For the first and second intervals, the average currents would be

1st 15 min:

$$\text{Average current} = \frac{1,200}{900} = 1.33 \text{ amp}$$

2nd 15 min:

$$\text{Average current} = \frac{2,400}{900} = 2.67 \text{ amp}$$

Further refinements are possible by using shorter measurement intervals, for example, 1 sec, 0.001 sec, or 10^{-6} sec. This leads to the notion of *instantaneous* current defined as the *limit* approached by the *average* current as the time interval over which the average is taken approaches zero. Thus, the instantaneous current is

$$i = \lim_{\Delta t \to 0} \frac{\Delta q}{\Delta t} = \frac{dq}{dt} \qquad [1]$$

Since current is the time derivative of charge transferred, then the amount of charge transferred over a period of time from t_1 to t_2 must be equal to the integral of the current over this time interval.

$$\Delta q = \int_{t_1}^{t_2} i(t) \, dt \qquad [2]$$

Let $q(t)$ be the charge transferred from $t = 0$ up to time t. The corresponding expression will be

$$q(t) = \int_0^t i(x) \, dx \qquad [3]$$

where x is just a dummy variable of integration.

In speaking of charges "moving through the hoop" something must be said of the direction of motion. This motion can be in either one direction or the other. So we arbitrarily choose a particular direction as the *reference*. If positive charges go through in that direction we say the current is positive; if they go in the opposite direction we say the current is negative. But how about negative charges? Suppose a positive and a negative charge of equal magnitude move at the same rate in the same direction. The *net* flow of charge will be zero. This means that a negative charge moving in one direction is equivalent to a positive charge of equal magnitude moving in the opposite direction. As long as the amount of charge transferred can be found, it is unimportant in defining current whether positive or negative charges move.

DEFINING A CURRENT REFERENCE
When charges are flowing in a discrete path, we *arbitrarily* assign a particular orientation along the path to be the *reference* orientation. The average current is called positive over a time interval if, during this time, the net charge transported along the reference orientation is positive or, equivalently, if the net charge transported opposite to the reference orientation is

negative. The reference orientation is indicated by an arrow drawn beside the path of charge flow.

In order to avoid the confusion of saying that positive charges move this way and negative charges move that way, it is customary and useful to assume that only positive charges are involved. Thus, when the current is positive, we say that charge (meaning *positive* charge) is *actually* flowing *along* the reference; and when the current is negative, we say that charge (meaning *positive* charge) is *actually* flowing *opposite to* the reference.

With respect to current, the term *orientation* will be used instead of *direction*. This is a more accurate description because the current path can be curved and accordingly not have a single direction, as shown in the illustration below. Over part

of the path, the *direction* of charge flow is horizontal while over the rest of the path the direction is vertical. Yet the *orientation* is the same over all parts of the path, as indicated by the arrows. When there is no possibility of ambiguity, instead of saying *current reference orientation*, we shall simply say *current reference*.

(If you need help in answering any of the following, reread Ref. Sec. 2.)

3 REFERENCE ORIENTATION FOR CURRENT
Let the current in the wire shown in the sketch below be la-

beled *i*. At a particular time, suppose $i = 2$ amp. What else is needed to completely describe the current in the wire?

In the diagram shown below, the current reference orientation is shown by the arrow. At a particular time, the actual current flow is 3 amp to the right. Then, $i =$ _____ amp.

At another time, $i = -4$ amp. The actual current at this time is to the _____ (left/right).

Electrons are moving up in the wire shown below, and an

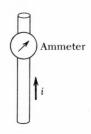

ammeter reads 5 amp. The current i, having the reference orientation shown by the arrow, is (check one):

(a)   +5

(b)   −5

(c)   Cannot be given, because the actual current is down

Is the following statement true or false?

The reference orientation for current in a wire must be chosen along the actual direction of positive charge flow.

An unknown current is flowing in the wire shown below.

What does the arrow indicate about the actual orientation of current at a specific given time? (Check one.)

(a)   Nothing.

(b)   The arrow shows the actual current orientation at that time.

In the vertical wire shown below, there is an actual current of 3 ma (milliamperes) flowing upward at some instant. Choose a reference orientation and show it by an arrow on the diagram, and specify i in terms of that reference: $i =$ _____

Since the reference is arbitrary, either orientation will do

$i = -3$ $i = +3$

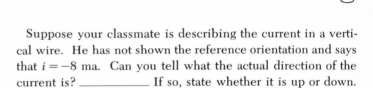

Suppose your classmate is describing the current in a vertical wire. He has not shown the reference orientation and says that $i = -8$ ma. Can you tell what the actual direction of the current is? _____ If so, state whether it is up or down.

No
Can't tell without a reference

The figure below shows a wire and its current reference.

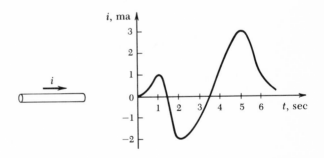

Also shown is a graph of the variation of current i with time. From the graph, state the value and actual direction of the current at instants indicated in the following table.

(a) 1; right

(b) −2; left

(c) 3; right

	Time, sec	i, ma	Left/right
(a)	$t = 1$		
(b)	2		
(c)	5		

The graph shown below is the current i in a horizontal wire. The reference orientation of the current is also shown.

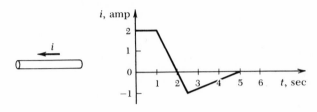

The actual orientation of the current at $t = 1$ sec is to the _____ (left/right). The numerical value is $i = $ _____ amp.

The actual orientation of the current at $t = 4$ sec is to the _____ (left/right). The numerical value is $i = $ _____ amp.

4 FLOW OF CHARGE

Let us now compute the charge flow over different time intervals. Refer to Ref. Sec. 2 if necessary.

For the same current as in the preceding diagram (repeated here below), it is desired to compute the charge flow during the interval from $t = 1$ to 2 sec. The first step is to find the

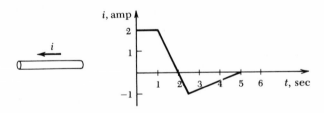

equation for $i(t)$. In this interval, the graph is a straight line described by the equation

$$i(t) = -2t + 4$$

The charge flow in the direction of the reference arrow during this interval will be

$$\Delta q = \int_{1}^{2}(-2t + 4)\,dt = (-t^2 + 4t)\Big|_{1}^{2} = 1 \text{ coul}$$

Similarly, compute the charge flow over the intervals indicated below:

Current equation   Charge flow

$t = 0$ to 1 sec

(a) $i(t) =$ $\Delta q =$

$t = 2.5$ to 5 sec

(b) $i(t) =$ $\Delta q =$

(a) $2; \int_{0}^{1} 2\,dt = 2$

(b) $\frac{2}{5}t - 2; \int_{\frac{5}{2}}^{5}\left(\frac{2}{5}t - 2\right)dt$

$= -\frac{5}{4}$

Inasmuch as electrons are the actual mobile charges in the wire, describe how many electrons move, and in what direction, during the interval from $t = 1$ to $t = 2$. _____

6.25×10^{18}

left; right

electrons move from _____ (left/right) to _____ (left/right).

Recalling the interpretation of the definite integral as "the area under the curve," the charge transferred in the interval $t = 1$ to 2 in the previous graph is the area of the triangle $(hb/2)$ having height h of 2 amp and base b of $2 - 1 = 1$ sec. This gives a charge of _____ coul.

1

Using the concept of an integral as an area, find the charge transferred between $t = 0$ and 1 and verify that it is the same as found before. The result is _____

area of rectangle of height 2 amp and base 1 sec = 2 coul

Suppose the current i of the previous graph is due to the motion of negative charge. In the interval from $t = 0$ to 5, _____ coul of negative charge will flow toward the _____ (right/left).

$2 + 1 - \frac{1 \times 3}{2} = \frac{3}{2}$

right (the equivalent positive charge is transferred along the reference, to the left)

The figure below shows the graph of the positive charge q transferred along a path by a current i having the reference orientation shown.

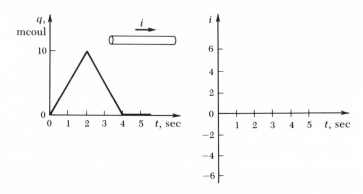

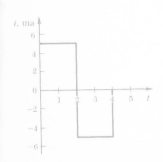

On the axes provided, draw a graph of the current i as a function of t. Label the ordinate with the appropriate unit of current. What are the values of i at $t = 1$ and $t = 3$?

(a) $t = 1$ $i = $ _____

(b) $t = 3$ $i = $ _____

(a) 5

(b) −5

What is the actual orientation of i at each of these times (is it *along* or *opposite to* the reference orientation)?

(a) At $t = 1$ sec: _____

(b) At $t = 3$ sec: _____

(a) along

(b) opposite to

The reference orientation for the current in a certain wire is chosen to the right. It is found that the expression for the charge conducted along the wire as a function of time is $q = 2(3t - 8)^2$ μcoul from $t = 0$ to 4. How many coulombs is 1 μcoul? _____ Find an expression for the current as a function of time; include unit of measure.

10^{-6}

$12(3t - 8)$ μamp

_____

Under the same conditions, $q(t)$ is given by one of the following. Write the corresponding expression for $i(t)$ but with the unit of measure given as amperes.

(a) $q(t) = \dfrac{100t}{t - 5}$ μcoul $(0 < t < 4)$

(a) $\dfrac{-5 \times 10^{-4}}{(t - 5)^2}$

$i(t) = $

(b) 0.4 cos 5t

(b) $q(t) = 80 \sin 5t$ mcoul

   $i(t) =$

The current along a vertical path is given by $i(t) = 10 \cos \pi t/2$ and is sketched below. The current reference is chosen to be downward. Find the charge transferred along the refer-

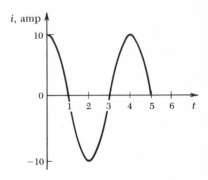

ence direction from $t = 0$ to 1 sec.

$\dfrac{20}{\pi}$

$q =$ _____ coul

If the charges that constitute the current are negative, over the interval from 0 to 1 sec they actually move _____ (up/down).

up

Find the net charge transferred along the path over the following intervals, and state whether the net motion of negative charges has actually been up or down.

(a) $\dfrac{-20}{\pi}$; down

(a) $t = 0$ to 3:

(b) $\dfrac{40}{\pi}$; up

(b) $t = 3$ to 5:

5 NETWORKS AND KIRCHHOFF'S CURRENT LAW
(REFERENCE SECTION)

We use the term *electric network* to describe an interconnection of electric devices, such as transistors, batteries, resistors, and transformers. An example is shown in Fig. 1. It is made up of a number of different devices.

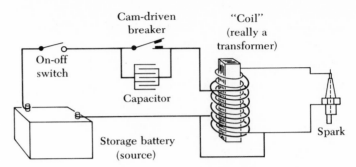

Fig. 1   Example of an Electrical Network (Automobile
        Ignition System).

The devices that form a network may be connected to each
other by metallic wires that conduct electricity well. These
connecting wires also exhibit many of the electrical characteristics of electrical devices—such as, the conversion of electrical
energy into heat or the storage of electrical energy—but usually
to a much smaller extent.

When we study the electrical behavior of a network, we often
concentrate on the *major* effects due to the devices themselves,
rather than on the *minor* effects due to the connecting wires.
At these times, we neglect the effects of the wires. On a diagram, we draw lines between various electrical devices to
represent the connections. These lines indicate only that there
is a connection; no other electrical behavior is implied.

The electrical effects then are considered to be concentrated,
or *lumped*, within the electrical devices. Often the specific
type of device in a network is not of interest, only its *presence*
in the network. This can be shown in a diagram as a simple
rectangle, or box, like this:

It is possible to take into account even the minor electrical
effects of the connecting wires by assuming these effects are
lumped, and then to insert appropriate boxes within the network to account for these effects. This is illustrated in Fig. 2.
An electric heater plugged into a wall socket is shown at (*a*).
The socket acts as an electric source. The electrical effect of
the heater is represented by a device called a *resistor*. You

have no doubt observed that the heater cord (the connecting wire) also heats up somewhat when the heater is operating. This can be represented by another lumped resistor.

The entire network can then be represented by the diagram in Fig. 2b. Here three boxes, which represent the wall socket, the heater, and the cord, are connected by lines that show the connections but have no other electrical effects.

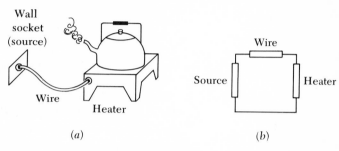

(a)   (b)

Fig. 2

Since a "paper network" like Fig. 2b is idealized to the extent of assuming that the electrical effects of all connecting wires can be placed inside the boxes, such a network is also called an *ideal* network. Thus, an ideal network is to be distinguished from the *physical* network that it represents, for example, Fig. 2a. In the following, whenever the word "network" is used without a modifier, it will mean "ideal network."

A network using boxes to represent electrical devices is shown in Fig. 3. Whatever the actual device, any box that has *two* terminals to which connections can be made in a network is called a *branch*.

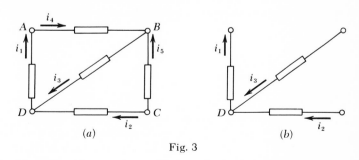

(a)   (b)

Fig. 3

The place where two or more branches are joined together is called a *junction*.

To show the reference orientation for the current in a branch, an arrow is placed alongside the branch, or an arrowhead is placed right on the branch itself. Thus, either of the following

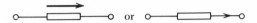

is permissible.

A given network will have a number of junctions. Consider a single junction in the network shown in Fig. 3a, for instance, the one labeled D at the lower left. This portion of the network is isolated from the rest and redrawn as Fig. 3b. A question can be asked as to whether there is any relationship among the currents i_1, i_2, and i_3. Generally speaking, these currents vary with time, but there is a relationship among them at each instant of time expressed by *Kirchhoff's current law*, abbreviated KCL.

For each junction in a network, the algebraic sum of all currents leaving the junction is zero at each instant of time.

For junction D, the application of Kirchhoff's current law leads to $i_1 - i_2 - i_3 = 0$. Minus signs appear before i_2 and i_3 because the reference orientations of i_2 and i_3 are *toward* the junction, and the left-hand side of the equation is the algebraic sum of currents *leaving* the junction.

6   APPLICATION OF KIRCHHOFF'S CURRENT LAW

junction

branch

In the network shown below, the part labeled A is a _____.
The part labeled B is a _____

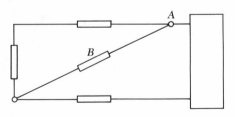

List the branches and junctions in the diagram below.

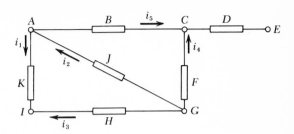

(a) Branches:
     B, D, F, H, J, K

(b) Junctions: A, C, G, I.
     (E is *not* a junction,
     since two or more
     branches are not
     connected there.)

ideal

two

$i_3 - i_4 - i_5 = 0$

A: $i_1 - i_2 + i_5 = 0$

I: $-i_1 - i_3 = 0$

G: $i_2 + i_3 + i_4 = 0$

(a) Branches: _____

(b) Junctions: _____

Each of the above networks is _____ (ideal/physical)

A branch has _____ (how many?) terminals.

Apply Kirchhoff's current law as given in the preceding section to junction B in Fig. 3, and write an expression relating the currents.

_____

Write similar expressions for KCL at junctions A, I, and G of the above figure.

At A: _____

At I: _____

At G: _____

The diagram below shows an isolated junction which is part of an extensive network not shown. Write a KCL expression relating the four currents.

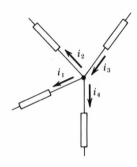

$i_1 + i_2 - i_3 + i_4 = 0$

Suppose the reference of i_2 is now reversed. Write the new KCL expression relating the currents.

$i_1 - i_2 - i_3 + i_4 = 0$

Part of a network with three branches connected to a junction is shown below. The given references are all directed away from the junction.

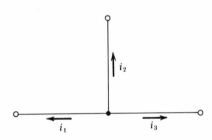

False.

References are arbitrary. They do not specify *actual* directions of current at any given time.

State whether the following is true or false, and why: "This choice of references is impossible because all of the currents cannot leave the junction." _____ (true/false)

In the previous diagram:

(a)   Apply KCL and write an equation relating i_1, i_2, and i_3.

_____

(b)   Solve this equation for i_3 in terms of i_1 and i_2 in literal form.

$i_3 =$ _____

Suppose $i_1 = 2$ ma and $i_2 = 3$ ma at some particular time?

(c)   Find the numerical value of i_3 at the given time and specify the unit of measure.

$i_3 =$ _____

(d)   What are the *actual* orientations of i_1, i_2, and i_3 at that time?

i_1: _____ (away from/toward) junction
i_2: _____ (away from/toward) junction
i_3: _____ (away from/toward) junction

The diagram below shows an isolated junction which is part of a more extensive network. Write a KCL expression relating the four currents.

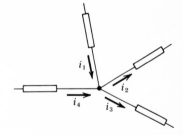

_____

(a) $i_1 + i_2 + i_3 = 0$

(b) $i_3 = -i_1 - i_2$

(c) $i_3 = -2 - 3 = -5$ ma

(d) i_1: away from
      i_2: away from
      i_3: toward

$-i_1 + i_2 + i_3 - i_4 = 0$

Numerical values of three of the currents corresponding to conditions existing at different instants of time, are given in the table below. Find the value of the missing current, and insert it into the appropriate column; also fill in each of the spaces of the two columns on the right.

i_1	i_2	i_3	i_4	Sum of currents actually leaving°	Sum of currents actually entering°
2	2	5	5	7	7
−1		0.5	3		
	−4	1	−3		
−5	−2	−1			

°Note the sum of currents whose references are leaving/entering.

In each case, is it true that the *actual* current leaving the junction equals the *actual* current entering it? _____

The fact that the sum of currents actually entering a junction equals the sum of currents actually leaving it means that, over a given time interval, the *amount of charge* actually entering the junction will equal the amount of charge actually leaving it. This means that charge _____ (can/cannot) accumulate at the junction. Thus, Kirchhoff's current law is equivalent to the physical principle of the *conservation of charge.*

7 JUNCTION REFERENCE (REMARK)

The original statement of KCL referred to the currents *leaving* a junction. The word "leaving" (or "away from") can be called the *junction reference.* It is also possible to state KCL as: "The algebraic sum of the currents *toward* a junction equals zero." In that case the junction reference is "toward." Each term in the equation will now have its sign changed. Changing the junction reference is equivalent to the operation of multiplying both sides of the equation by −1. There is nothing fundamentally different in the new equation. It gives the same information as before. For uniformity, we shall continue to take "away from" as the junction reference.

Leaving Entering
1.5   3   3
0   4   4
2   5   5

Yes

cannot

8 MORE ON REFERENCES

The diagram below shows a branch which is part of a network. The value of the current i at some particular time is given as -5 amp.

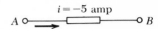

$$i = -5 \text{ amp}$$

$A \circ \longrightarrow B$

Check whichever of the following is correct:

(a) Because the value of the current is negative, the current reference is actually toward junction A.

(b) Because the value of the current is negative, its actual orientation at that time is toward junction A.

When the sign of a particular value of current is negative, the actual orientation of the current _____ (coincides with/is opposite to) its reference orientation.

In the diagram below, the current in the branch has been labeled both i_1 and i_2, with opposite references. Check any of

the following statements which are correct:

(a) This is impossible because current cannot actually flow with opposite orientations at the same time.

(b) This is possible, it just means that $i_2 = -i_1$.

(c) This could be used for an alternating current, which is sometimes oriented one way and sometimes the other, but not for a direct current.

9 ALTERNATE STATEMENT OF KCL

As Kirchhoff's current law is expressed in Ref. Sec. 5, the result is an algebraic sum of quantities equated to zero. (Some humorous student commented to the effect that, since the result of

KCL adds up to nothing, why bother with it in the first place!) It is always possible to transpose terms in an algebraic equation. Transposing i_2 and i_3 in the equation $i_1 - i_2 - i_3 = 0$ (Ref. Sec. 5) leads to

$$i_1 = i_2 + i_3$$

The reference orientation for i_1 is away from the junction; the reference orientations for i_2 and i_3 are toward the junction. Thus, another way of stating KCL is the following.

> *At a junction, the sum of all currents with branch references oriented away from the junction equals the sum of all currents with branch references oriented toward the junction.*

Use this form of KCL to write an equation for the junction shown below.

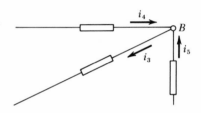

$i_3 = i_4 + i_5$

_____

Now write KCL in the original form with "leaving" as the junction reference. Then transpose terms and verify the above.

(a) $i_3 - i_4 - i_5 = 0$

(b) $i_3 = i_4 + i_5$

(a) Original: _____

(b) Transposed: _____

Use the latest statement of KCL to write expressions relating the currents in branches connected to junctions A, B, C, and D in the following diagram.

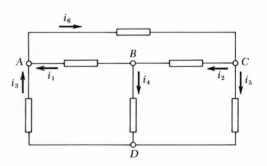

$A:\quad i_6 = i_1 + i_3$

$B:\quad i_1 + i_4 = i_2$

$C:\quad i_2 + i_5 = i_6$

$D:\quad i_3 = i_4 + i_5$

At A: _____

At B: _____

At C: _____

At D: _____

In the diagram below, find an expression for the unknown current i and its value when $t = 0.5$ sec.

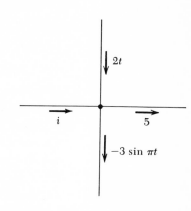

$-i - 2t + 5 - 3 \sin \pi t = 0$

$i = 5 - 2t - 3 \sin \pi t$

At $t = 0.5$, $i = 1$.

$i = $ _____
(expression)

$i = $ _____
(at $t = 0.5$)

toward
the junction

At $t = 0.5$, the actual orientation is _____
(toward/away from)

10 DOUBLE-SUBSCRIPT NOTATION

Another method of indication a current reference orientation is shown in the following diagram. The two ends of a branch

are labeled A and B, respectively. Designating the current i_{AB} means that the reference arrow is directed from A to B. Of course, with this *double-subscript notation*, we could also talk about i_{BA}. On the figure, show the reference arrow for i_{BA}.

How would i_{BA} be related to i_{AB}?

$-i_{AB}$

$i_{BA} =$ _____

In the diagram of the complete network in the last section, let the currents be designated with double-subscript notation consistent with the references shown there. Applying the first form of KCL, the equation for junction A becomes

$$i_{AC} - i_{BA} - i_{DA} = 0$$

By reversing the appropriate subscripts, this equation can be written so that all signs are positive. Thus,

$$i_{AC} + i_{AB} + i\_\_\_ = 0$$

AD

Write the KCL equations at junctions B, C, and D, taking *away from* as the junction reference and using double-subscript notation for the currents. Arrange the subscripts so that all terms will be positive.

B: $i_{BA} + i_{BD} + i_{BC} = 0$ At B: _____

C: $i_{CA} + i_{CB} + i_{CD} = 0$ At C: _____

D: $i_{DA} + i_{DB} + i_{DC} = 0$ At D: _____

11   REVIEW PROBLEMS
Complete each problem before verifying your answers.

PROBLEM 1
A current i_{AB} varies with time as shown in the graph below.

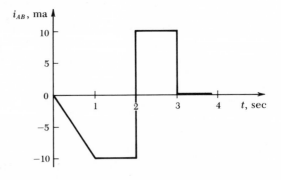

(a)   Over what time interval is the current actually oriented from A to B?

From $t =$ _____ to _____

(b)   Over what time interval is the current actually oriented from B to A?

From $t =$ _____ to _____

(c)   How much positive charge in coulombs passes from A to B in the interval $t = 0$ to 4 sec? Specify the unit of measure also.

Charge =

(d)   The number of electrons this represents is of the order of (encircle one):

(i) 3×10^5 (ii) 10^{10} (iii) 10^{16}

(e)   How much charge accumulates in the branch between A and B during the interval from $t = 0$ to $t = 1$ sec? _____

PROBLEM 2

Three branches are shown connected to a junction, in the figure below. Two of the branch current references are oriented toward the junction. The reference for the third current i_3 (check one):

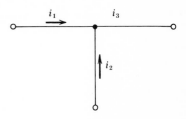

(a)   Must be away from the junction because some current must be leaving the junction, otherwise charge will be accumulating there.

(b)   Can be chosen either away from the junction or toward it.

PROBLEM 3

Three branches are connected at a junction as shown below.

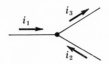

Fill in the blanks in the following table.

	i_1	i_2	i_3
(a)	-8	8	
(b)	-5		-2
(c)		$-2e^{-t}$	$-e^{-t}$

(a) 0

(b) 3

(c) e^{-t}

PROBLEM 4

Suppose the references of the currents in three branches connected at a junction are all directed away from the junction as shown below.

Appraise the following statement:

"This is not possible; if all these currents are flowing away from the junction, it will mean that current is being generated from nothing at the junction." _____ (true/false)

False. It is true that not all currents can *actually* be flowing away from the junction, but reference orientations do not necessarily coincide with actual orientations. Thus, when all reference orientations are directed away from the junction, the *values* of at least one of the currents will be negative at any particular time.

PROBLEM 5

At some particular time, the currents in the following diagram have the values shown.

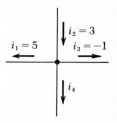

Find the value of i_4 at this time, and state whether its *actual* orientation is toward or away from the junction.

$$i_4 =$$

$i_1 - i_2 + i_3 + i_4 = 0$
$i_4 = -i_1 + i_2 - i_3 =$
$-5 + 3 + 1 = -1$

toward

Its orientation is _____ (toward/away from)

Suppose that, with nothing else changed, the reference orientation of i_1 in the preceding diagram is reversed.

(a) −5

(b) $i_4 = i_1 + i_2 - i_3$

(c) unchanged

(a)   The new value of i_1 will be $i_1 =$ _____
(b)   The literal expression for i_4 will be $i_4 =$ _____
(c)   The numerical value of i_4 will be _____ (unchanged/changed) in sign.

Based on the preceding, the following general statements can be made:

(a)   In a literal equation expressing KCL, changing a current reference orientation _____ (will/will not) require a change in sign of the corresponding term.

(b)   The numerical value of a branch current _____ (is/is not) influenced by the references chosen for the currents of other branches connected to that node.

12   REMARK

The original enunciation of the current law by Gustav Kirchhoff, a German scientist, was based on the experimental evidence obtained by measuring currents in branches that were connected together.   (This was in the 1840s.)   It has been pointed out earlier in the text that validity of the current law is equivalent to conservation of charge; that in an ideal network charge cannot accumulate or disappear at a junction. It is probably fortunate for the progress of electrical science that Kirchhoff's experiments were made with constant currents; because in the presence of a *time-varying* electric field, the charge on the junction of actual wires (in a physical network) can be varying, and the current law then does not hold. For example, in Fig. (a) below, the sum $i_1 + i_2 + i_3$ is not generally zero. However, about 25 years after Kirchhoff's current law was stated, Maxwell introduced the idea that a time-varying electric field can be viewed like a current in a capacitor. Thus, a paper model (ideal network) can be created as in Fig. (b) below, where the capacitor introduces a fourth current which results in $i_1 + i_2 + i_3 + i_4 = 0$. The junction in this ideal network has zero charge at all times.

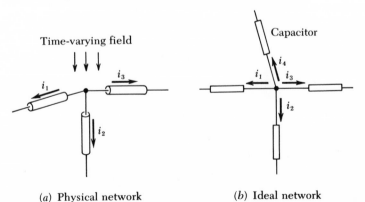

(a) Physical network   (b) Ideal network

In summary, although Kirchhoff originally enunciated his current law for situations where the charge would be constant on a junction, it can be used for the more general case by creating a model in which the time-varying nature of the charge on the physical junction is accounted for by the introduction of an additional branch (or possibly more) in the model. In this sense, Kirchhoff's current law is universally valid for ideal networks.

Voltage and Kirchhoff's Voltage Law

1 INTRODUCTION

The existence of electrical phenomena depends on electrical charges becoming separated, with some objects being positively charged and others negatively charged. Any of the various devices that act as sources (batteries, generators, thermocouples, etc.) have the fundamental property of being able to accumulate positive charge at one terminal and negative charge at the other terminal. When an external conducting path is provided between the terminals of a source, as in the figure below, the separated charges have a means of flowing back together to accomplish a recombination. Meanwhile, the source

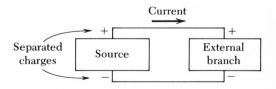

continues to cause charge separation, thus enabling a current to flow continuously. The situation is illustrated in the figure.

The concept of voltage is related to the changes in energy experienced by a charge as it moves through a circuit such as this.

2 DEFINITION OF VOLTAGE (REFERENCE SECTION)

Several types of forces act on charged particles in various parts of an electrical circuit (or network) and are pertinent to the electrical phenomena that occur. These forces can be classified as follows:

(a) Forces due to the presence of other charges. They are usually called electrostatic forces.

(b) Forces due to a time-varying magnetic field or due to the motion of a charged particle in a magnetic field.

(c) Forces that can be defined to represent chemical, thermo-dynamic, or quantum-mechanical phenomena (for example, in an electrolytic cell, thermocouple, or photocell).

(d) Frictionlike forces that represent the aggregate effect of inelastic collisions of a moving particle with "stationary" atoms and/or molecules.

Referring to the previous figure, if all forces except those of (a) can be considered to be confined to regions inside the boxes, it is permissible to view the arrangement as a circuit; otherwise, it must be analyzed as a "field" problem, by methods not within the scope of this text. This exception usually occurs when a magnetic field produces forces that cannot be localized in boxes. We shall define voltage as a circuit quantity. It is the quantity indicated by a voltmeter connected in a circuit or network, when the circuit viewpoint is valid.

In a source, forces of types (b) and (c) act to separate charges, doing work against the electrostatic force and thereby causing energy to be stored. The stored energy is called *electric potential energy* (or merely *potential energy*). The electrostatic force tends to cause separated charges to recombine; and when they recombine by flowing through an electrical device, the stored energy is converted to some other form of energy by virtue of the work done by the electrostatic force against forces of types (b), (c), or (d), or a combination of these.

The change in potential energy of a charged particle when it changes position is independent of the path it takes. In this respect, electric potential energy is like gravitational potential energy. For example, if you walk from one point on the side of a hill to another point at a different elevation, the work you do against the force of gravity (which equals the change in gravitational potential energy) will be independent of your route, even if you go to the bottom of the hill on the way. Since the change in potential energy is independent of the path between the two points, it is uniquely a function of those end points. In particular, if those end points are identical (that is, the path is closed) the change in potential energy "between them" must be zero. In other words, the work done by electrostatic forces acting on a charged particle over a closed path is always zero.

An electrostatic force exists at each point in a region of space where there are separated charges. The collection of all these forces is referred to as an *electrostatic field*, and so the phrases "work done by an electrostatic force" and "work done by an electrostatic field" are synonymous.

Now consider the box shown below. It is part of a network,

$$A \;\; \circ\!\!\!-\!\!\!\boxed{}\!\!\!-\!\!\!\circ \;\; B$$

the remainder of which is not shown. A state of charge separation exists in the network, and so electrostatic forces exist. To be specific, assume these forces act in the direction from A to B. Imagine a particle, having positive charge q, located at point A. It could have arrived there by having been pushed through a source or moved in some way through the air from B to A. By virtue of the property of the electrostatic force noted above, the potential energy of the charge is the same, whatever the route by which q got to B. Now imagine the charge moving through the box. Its potential energy will *decrease* (because it moves in the direction of the electrostatic force) by an amount that we shall call W_{AB}. This is also the amount of work done by the electrostatic field in moving q from A to B and is equal to the work previously done by some unspecified agent when moving the charge from B to A.

If q is very small, so that its motion does not disturb the distribution of other charges (which are not shown), the decrease of potential energy W_{AB} will be proportional to q. We assume this to be the case. Then, the quantity

$$V_{AB} = \frac{W_{AB}}{q}$$

is unique; that is, it is independent of q (so long as q is very small). From the form of the equation, it is seen that V_{AB} is the decrease in potential energy per unit charge from A to B; but it is customary to drop the words "energy" and "per unit charge" and call it merely *potential decrease* from A to B. This potential decrease is also called the *voltage* from A to B. The unit of voltage is the *volt*; it is equivalent to a joule per coulomb.

The order of the subscripts (A to B, for example) is related to the direction the "test charge" q is imagined to move. This point is emphasized because, in the example given here, the direction of the electrostatic force is also from A to B; and W_{AB} and V_{AB} are positive numbers. In the event the electrostatic force is from B to A, we can still speak of the voltage from A to B, but W_{AB} and V_{AB} will be negative numbers.

Observe that the small charge q used in the imagined experiment is a test charge invented for the purpose of defining voltage. It may or may not be a particle that constitutes part of a current. For example, in the figure shown in Sec. 1, although the current direction is "up" through the source and "down" through the external branch, in defining the voltage across the source the test charge may be imagined to move downward.

3 VOLTAGE AND ENERGY

The figure below shows a hypothetical experiment in which a small positively charged body is immersed in oil. A and B are two charged metal plates. Suppose the positive charge is $q = 2 \times 10^{-5}$ coul and that the small body moves at a constant velocity from A to B under the influence of the electrostatic field due to the charged plates. Let the average frictional force acting on the charge be 6×10^{-4} newtons.

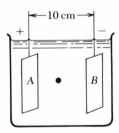

The work done by the electrostatic force in the process
equals _____ joules.

6×10^{-5}

The small circle in the diagram below represents the small

(Net force = 0)

charged particle above. The arrow shows the direction of the
electrostatic force on the particle. Draw another arrow (dashed)
to indicate the direction of the force on the charged particle due
to friction in the oil.

3 volts

The potential decrease from A to B equals _____
(include unit of measure).

3 volts

The voltage from A to B equals _____ (include
unit of measure).

The figure below illustrates a piece of wire bent into an arc
(for no particular reason). Let the potential decrease from P to
Q be 24 volts.

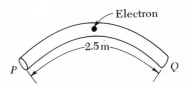

The electrostatic field will expend energy by virtue of the
motion of electrons. A sample electron is shown in an intermediate position. The electron will move from _____
(P to Q/Q to P).

Q to P

Recalling that the magnitude of the charge of an electron is
1.6×10^{-19} coul, the work done by the field in moving one
electron throughout the length of the wire equals _____
joules. The average frictional force on the electron as it moves
from Q to P equals _____ newtons.

38.4×10^{-19}

15.36×10^{-19}

If a current of 0.5 amp flows continuously through the wire,
how much work is done by the field in 0.20 sec?

2.4 joules

Work = _____ (include unit of measure)

Suppose a positive charge of 2 coul moves from point R to
point S in an electrostatic field. If the field does 25 joules of
work, the voltage is $V_{RS} =$ _____ (include the algebraic sign and give the unit of measure).

$+ 12.5$ volts

If there is a voltage $v_{AB} = -100$ volts between two points
A and B, and the decrease in potential energy in moving a
charge from A to B is 20 joules, give the value, sign, and unit
of measure of the charge.

$q = \dfrac{W_{AB}}{v_{AB}} = \dfrac{20}{-100}$

$q =$

$= -0.2$ coul

If the voltage from P to Q is positive, we say that point P is
at a higher potential than point Q. Let a point P be at a higher
potential than a point Q. When a negative charge moves from P

increase

to Q, the potential energy will _____ (increase/
decrease).

In the diagram below $v_{AB} = 10$ volts. A positive charge of 0.01

$A \circ\!\!-\!\!\boxed{}\!\!-\!\!\circ B$

decreases

0.1

coul moves from A to B. The potential energy _____
(increases/decreases) by _____ joules.

lower

If the potential energy is decreased when a negative charge
moves from P to Q then point P is actually at a _____
(higher/lower) potential than point Q.

When a certain charge of 2 coul moves between two points,
from A to B, the potential energy is changed by 10 joules. It
is desired to find the voltage v_{AB} if the charge is *positive* and
the potential energy is *increased*. To solve the problem, note

minus (negative decrease)

plus

-5

that $v_{AB} = W_{AB}/q$. Thus, the value of W_{AB} is _____
(plus/minus) 10 joules. The value of q is _____
(plus/minus) 2 coul. Hence, $v_{AB} =$ _____ volts.

For the same situation, find v_{AB} under the following conditions (use the same numerical values):

(a) +5 volts

(a) The charge is positive and the potential energy is de-
     creased. $v_{AB} =$ _____

(b) −5 volts

(b) The charge is negative and the potential energy is de-
     creased. $v_{AB} =$ _____

(c) +5 volts

(c) The charge is negative and the potential energy is in-
     creased. $v_{AB} =$ _____

4 NOTATION FOR VOLTAGE (REFERENCE SECTION)

Since the definition of voltage involves two points, there must be some method of designating *from* which point *to* which point there is a potential decrease. This can be done with the use of double subscripts. Thus, on the following diagram of a network

$$A \circ \!\!-\!\!\!\!\square\!\!\!-\!\!\circ B$$

branch, v_{AB} specifies the potential decrease *from* A, the first subscript, to B, the second subscript. In a particular situation, v_{AB} may turn out to be positive, or it may turn out to be negative. If v_{AB} is positive, it means that there is *actually* a decrease in potential in going from A to B. In this case, point A is at a *higher* potential. If v_{AB} is negative, it means that there is *actually* an increase in potential in moving from A to B; so point A is at a lower potential.

Even though—in the definition of voltage—there is the idea of motion of a *test charge* from one point to another, unlike current, voltage *does not* "flow." We say "the current *through* such and such a branch," but we cannot use the same word for voltage since it does not "flow through." We say, instead, "the voltage *across* the branch," For voltage, the word *polarity* corresponds to what is called the "direction of flow" in the case of current. When we were speaking of current, however, we introduced the term *orientation* to replace "direction," because it describes the situation more accurately. We shall use the same word, "orientation," to stand for polarity. In this way, we can refer to the orientation of both current and voltage, even though for current its meaning is "direction" and for voltage its meaning is "polarity."

The double-subscript notation is cumbersome. Another way of designating the initial and final point in the definition of voltage is to use + and − markings, as in the following diagram, together with a symbol for voltage, say v. If we write v and put

$$A \circ \overset{+}{\underset{}{\!\!-\!\!\!\!\square\!\!\!-\!\!}} \overset{v}{} \overset{-}{} \circ B$$

a plus sign at point A and a minus sign at point B, it is the same as writing v_{AB}.[†]

[†] Of course the plus sign alone is sufficient, since the other point will carry a minus sign by implication. Similarly, any other mark, or pair of marks, could be used. It is customary, however, for a dc voltmeter to carry a plus sign on one terminal. If a voltmeter is connected across the above branch so that the plus sign on the voltmeter and the plus mark on the branch coincide, then the voltmeter will read upscale when v is positive.

The plus and minus signs (or just the plus sign) constitute a *reference orientation* for the voltage. This reference orientation is *arbitrarily* chosen. To specify the voltage reference orientation for a given branch is to specify at which terminal of the branch the plus sign is placed. If v is to be the voltage of a branch, it is necessary to show both the symbol v and its reference, namely, the plus (or plus and minus) sign, as shown in the following diagram. In this diagram, with the reference shown, v is the same as v_{BA}. In the preceding diagram, because

$$A \circ \!\!-\!\!\overset{-\quad v \quad +}{\fbox{ }}\!\!-\!\!\circ B$$

the reference was different, v was the same as v_{AB}. Of course, v is an algebraic quantity that may be positive or negative. When v is positive, the *actual* polarity of the voltage is the same as its reference orientation. When v is negative the *actual* voltage polarity is opposite to its reference.

5   REFERENCE ORIENTATION FOR VOLTAGE

Let the voltage across a branch be v. At a particular time, suppose $v = 5$ volts.

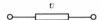

What else is needed to make the definition of v unique?

A reference mark

_____

In the diagram below, the symbol v stands for the potential

decrease

_____ (increase/decrease) from B to A.

$$A \circ \!\!-\!\!\overset{-\quad v \quad +}{\fbox{ }}\!\!-\!\!\circ B$$

A flashlight cell has its positive terminal at the center and its voltage is 1.5 volts. This statement is a description of the

actual

_____ (reference/actual) polarity. The diagram below shows two top views of such a cell, with two reference orientations.

Which of the following is correct?

(a) $v_2 = 1.5$ volts; v_1 is impossible because the polarity is wrong.

(b) $v_2 = 1.5$ volts; $v_1 = -1.5$ volts.

With the labeling of the terminals shown below, v_{CD} is the same as _____ (v_1/v_2). Its value is _____ volts.

At a given time, suppose the potential of point A in the following figure is higher than that of point B. The reference orientation for v (check one):

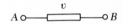

(a) Must be chosen with the plus sign at A

(b) Can be chosen with the plus sign at either A or B

Just as there are two directions in which the current can actually flow in a branch, there are two possibilities for the

actual _____ of the voltage.

With reference to the diagram below, suppose that at a particular time $v = -2$ volts. At this time, the *actual* polarity of the

voltage is positive at the _____ (top/bottom). It _____ (coincides with/is opposite to) the reference polarity.

Suppose $v = 3$ volts at a later time. At this time, the actual polarity of the voltage _____ (coincides with/is opposite to) the reference. The actual polarity is positive at

the _____ (top/bottom).

In the diagram below, suppose that the left-hand terminal is at a higher potential than the right-hand terminal at a given

time. The reference + sign (check one):

(a) Must be placed on the left
(b) Can be placed at either terminal

The graph below shows the variation of the voltage for the branch having the reference shown. State the interval of time

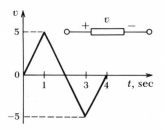

over which the actual polarity:

(a) Coincides with the reference orientation. ___ < t < ___
(b) Is opposite to the reference orientation. ___ < t < ___

At a particular time, if a certain voltage $v_{AB} = 10$ volts, then $v_{BA} = $ _____

If the *decrease* of potential from F to G is negative, which point, F or G, is actually at a higher potential? _____

Place a voltage reference plus sign on the branch shown below, so that with that reference $v = v_{BA}$. v_{BA} is the voltage _____ (through/across) the branch.

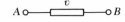

If a voltage is to be defined, there must be (check one):

(a) Two points
(b) A branch joining two points for the voltage to go through

Is the following statement true or false? "Like current, voltage flows between two points." _____

<!-- margin answers -->
(b)

(a) 0 < t < 2
(b) 2 < t < 4

−10 volts

G

across

+ at B

(a)

False

6 VOLTAGES SUMMED ALONG DIFFERENT PATHS

The decrease in potential energy of a test charge as it moves from one point to another is *independent* of the path between the two points. This means that if we imagine taking a test charge from A to C in the following figure, either through the intermediate point B *or* directly (along the dashed line), the work done will be the same.

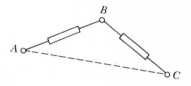

Express the voltage v_{AC}, regarded as the decrease of potential energy per unit charge along the dotted path between A and C, in terms of the voltages v_{AB} and v_{BC}.

$v_{AC} =$ _____

$v_{AB} + v_{BC}$

In the following figure, besides the direct path from A to C, there are now two other paths between these two points. Express v_{AC} in terms of the appropriate branch voltages along each of these paths.

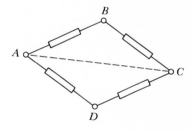

(a) $v_{AB} + v_{BC}$
(b) $v_{AD} + v_{DC}$

(a) $v_{AC} =$ _____
(b) $v_{AC} =$ _____

Since there are two equations for v_{AC}, the two can be equated to give

$v_{AB} + v_{DC}$

$v_{AB} + v_{BC} =$ _____

This last expression can be rewritten by transposing terms as follows

$$v_{AB} + v_{BC} - v_{DC} - v_{AD} = 0$$

But

$$v_{DA} = -v_{AD}$$

$$v_{CD} = \underline{\hspace{6cm}}$$

and, therefore, an equivalent form is

$$v_{AB} + v_{BC} + v_{CD} + v_{DA} = 0$$

The set of branches in the above diagram constitutes a *closed circuit*, or *loop*, and each term in the above equation is the potential decrease along one side of the loop. If, to arrive at the above equation, we imagine "going around" the circuit while writing down symbols for potential decreases across successive branches, which is the starting point? $\underline{\hspace{3cm}}$.

Which is the ending point? $\underline{\hspace{3cm}}$. Are they the

same? $\underline{\hspace{6cm}}$

7   KIRCHHOFF'S VOLTAGE LAW

The last equation illustrates the general fact that the sum of the potential decreases (or voltages) encountered in traversing (going around) a closed loop is equal to zero. This is a general result which holds for any closed path. It is a direct result of the fact, stated in Ref. Sec. 2, that potential energy is unchanged when a test charge is taken over any arbitrary path that returns to the starting point. It can be stated as follows.

Around any closed loop, the algebraic sum of all voltages (potential decreases) in the direction of traversal (either clockwise or counterclockwise) is zero at each instant of time.

This is a statement of *Kirchhoff's voltage law* (abbreviated KVL).

In the diagram below using double subscripts, KVL applied to the loop *ABCA* can be written

$$v_{AB} + v_{BC} + v_{CA} = 0$$

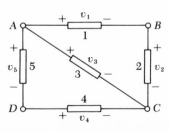

Write similar expressions for the other two loops in the network.

(a) $v_{AC} + v_{CD} + v_{DA} = 0$

(b) $v_{AB} + v_{BC} + v_{CD} + v_{DA} = 0$

(a) Loop $ACDA$: _____

(b) Loop $ABCDA$: _____

In the preceding diagram, the branch voltages are also labeled with single numerical subscripts, and reference orientations are shown. Working from the diagram, Kirchhoff's voltage law written for loop $ABCA$ (clockwise) in terms of these voltages will be

$$v_1 + v_2 - v_3 = 0$$

The third term carries a minus sign, because (from the diagram) the potential *decrease* v_{CA} from C to A across branch 3 is (in terms of v_3)

$-v_3$

$$v_{CA} = \underline{\hspace{4cm}}$$

Write similar expressions for KVL applied to the other two loops in the network (go clockwise).

(a) $v_3 - v_4 - v_5 = 0$

(b) $v_1 + v_2 - v_4 - v_5 = 0$

(a) Loop $ACDA$: _____

(b) Loop $ABCDA$: _____

Suppose the reference for v_4 is reversed and all else remains the same. Show how these equations are changed by rewriting them for the new condition.

(a) $v_3 + v_4 - v_5 = 0$

(b) $v_1 + v_2 + v_4 - v_5 = 0$

(a) Loop $ACDA$: _____

(b) Loop $ABCDA$: _____

If the reference for v_4 is as originally specified but v_2 is reversed, rewrite below any of these equations that will be changed.

$v_1 - v_2 - v_4 - v_5 = 0$

_____

In describing the voltage v_5 in the preceding diagram, we say

across

it is the voltage _____ (across/through) branch 5.

In the statement of Kirchhoff's current law, we identified either "away from" or "toward" as the *junction reference.* Similarly, for the voltage law, we identify the direction of traversing the *loop* as the *loop reference* orientation. In the

clockwise

counterclockwise

statement of KVL the loop reference can be either _____ or _____.

In the case of a voltage, we say the reference of a branch voltage *coincides with* the loop reference if the + marked terminal of the branch is the first one encountered when traversing the loop; otherwise, the branch and loop references

are opposite. By analogy with the current law, in writing KVL around a loop, if the reference of a branch voltage v_x is *opposite to* the loop reference, v_x will appear in the expression with a
_____ sign; if the branch reference coincides with the loop reference, v_x will appear with a _____
sign.

minus

plus

Write the expression for Kirchhoff's voltage law for the closed path shown in the diagram below, starting at X; specify the loop reference you used.

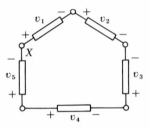

(a) $v_1 + v_2 - v_3 - v_4 + v_5 = 0$

(b) Clockwise. (Change all signs for counterclockwise.)

(a) Equation: _____

(b) Loop Reference: _____

In the diagram below, three branches form a closed path.

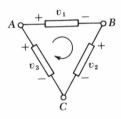

Suppose we choose to write Kirchhoff's voltage law using a clockwise loop reference, as indicated by the curved arrow. Starting at A, the reference for v_1 coincides with the loop reference; hence, v_1 will appear with a positive sign in KVL. The reference for v_2 coincides with the loop reference, so it will appear with a _____ sign. The reference for v_3 is opposite to the loop reference, so it will appear with a _____ sign.

positive

negative

The expression for KVL will, therefore, be _____

$v_1 + v_2 - v_3 = 0$

Apply KVL to the closed loop in the diagram below.

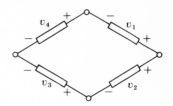

(a) $-v_1 + v_2 + v_3 - v_4 = 0$

(b) $v_1 - v_2 - v_3 + v_4 = 0$

(a) Clockwise: _____

(b) Counterclockwise: _____

In the diagram below the branches form a closed loop.

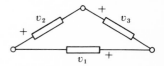

The reference for each of the three voltages coincides with a clockwise loop orientation.

(a) At any given time, is it possible for all of the actual voltages to be positive? _____
Why or why not? _____

(a) No

The sum would not be zero.

(b) Is it true or false that the references cannot be chosen as shown? _____ Why? _____

(b) False. References are arbitrary.

(c) Suppose at a given time that v_1 and v_2 are both positive. The actual polarity of v_3 will _____ (coincide with/be opposite to) its reference orientation.

(c) be opposite to

8 SOLVING FOR AN UNKNOWN VOLTAGE

As in the case of KCL, one of the branch voltages may be unknown and this unknown may be found in terms of the other branch voltages. This can be done by first expressing KVL as a summation of voltages around a loop. Alternatively, the path independence of the voltage between two points may be used by taking the two points to be the ends of the branch whose voltage is unknown. One expression for the voltage between the two points is simply the voltage of the branch. Another expression for the same voltage is the sum of the voltages of the branches which form a loop with that branch.

In the diagram below, v_5 is the voltage v_{BA}. But v_{BA} also equals $v_{BC} + v_{CA} = v_4 - v_1$. Hence,

$$v_5 = v_4 - v_1$$

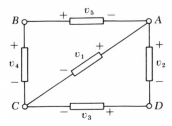

Find another expression for v_5 in the same way, using another set of branches forming a loop with branch 5.

$v_4 - v_3 - v_2$

$v_5 = $ _____

Using the same approach, for the same diagram find two expressions for v_2

(a) $v_1 - v_3$

(b) $-v_5 + v_4 - v_3$

(a) $v_2 = $ _____

(b) $v_2 = $ _____

The following diagram shows a closed loop which is part of a more extensive network. Numerical values of three of the

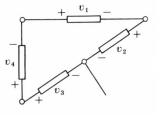

voltages, corresponding to conditions existing at different instants of time, are given in the following table. Find the value of the missing voltage and fill in the appropriate column; also fill in the other two columns on the right.

v_1	v_2	v_3	v_4	Sum of voltages with polarities actually clockwise°	Sum of voltages with polarities actually ccw°
5	10	12			
−2	8		−9		
	4	10	2		
−8	1		2		

°Not the sum of voltages whose references are cw/ccw.

In each case, how is the "sum of voltages with polarities actually clockwise" related to the "sum of voltages with polarities actually counterclockwise"? _____

9 REMARK

In a practical situation, it is possible for a physical network to be immersed in a time-varying magnetic field. In such a case, electrical forces of type (b) come into play that are not accounted for in the Kirchhoff voltage law equations. Hence, KVL must then be modified. However, we are considering ideal networks for which it is assumed that closed paths do not surround time-varying magnetic fields.

Reference is again made to the work of Kirchhoff. He enunciated the voltage law as a result of his work with physical networks. But he used constant currents; therefore, the associated magnetic fields were constant. It may thus be said that the origin of KVL was a happy accident, arising from the fact that Kirchhoff dealt with constant currents. Ideal networks can represent practical cases when time-varying magnetic fields are present; but to do this requires the results of the original research done by Michael Faraday (1791-1867) in England, and Joseph Henry (1797–1878) in the United States.

10 REVIEW PROBLEM

The following diagram shows 5 branches connected to form an electric network. (The diagram has been drawn twice to avoid confusion between references for voltage and for current.)

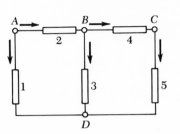 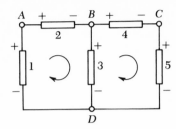

(a) Write KCL equations at the nodes A, B, and C, taking "leaving the node" as the reference. Do this using the numbers at the boxes as single numerical subscripts, and with double-subscript notation.

A: $i_1 + i_2 = 0$
$i_{AB} + i_{AD} = 0$

At A: _____

B: $-i_2 + i_3 + i_4 = 0$
$i_{BA} + i_{BD} + i_{RC} = 0$

At B: _____

C: $-i_4 + i_5 = 0$
$i_{CR} + i_{CD} = 0$

At C: _____

(b) Write KVL equations around the two loops identified by the solid curved arrows, with "clockwise" as loop reference. Do this both with numerical subscripts and with double-subscript notation.

(i) $-v_1 + v_2 + v_3 = 0$

(ii) $v_{DA} + v_{AB} + v_{BD} = 0$

(i) $-v_3 + v_4 + v_5 = 0$

(ii) $v_{DR} + v_{BC} + v_{CD} = 0$

Left loop: (i) _____
                (ii) _____
Right loop: (i) _____
                (ii) _____

(c) Using the fact the voltage is independent of path, write an expression for v_5 in terms of branch voltages on the outer loop consisting of branches 1, 2, 4, and 5. Do this directly from the diagram. Write your answer twice, in terms of numerical subscripts, and double subscripts.

(i) $v_5 = -v_4 - v_2 + v_1$

(ii) $v_5 = -v_{BC} - v_{AB} + v_{AD}$

(i) $v_5 = $ _____
(ii) $v_5 = $ _____

(d) Add the two KVL equations in part (b), then solve for v_5. Compare with the result in (c). Does the KVL equation of the outer loop convey any more information than that contained in the set of KVL equations of the other two loops?

_____

Ohm's Law, Sources and Power

1 INTRODUCTION

Many electrical devices (such as, batteries, heaters, and neon lamps) have two terminals. Each device, when connected in a network, will have associated with it a current and a voltage. In the ideal representation, currents will satisfy Kirchhoff's current law at each junction of the network. Similarly, the voltages of the branches of each loop will satisfy Kirchhoff's voltage law. These two laws are quite independent of each other. Nothing need be said of a branch voltage when applying the current law, and nothing need be said of a branch current when applying the voltage law.

However, for each electrical device there is a characteristic way in which the voltage and current of the device are related. For actual physical devices, these relationships can be discovered by simultaneous measurement of the voltage and current. Often, mathematical formulas relating the voltage and current of a device can be obtained by carrying out an analysis of the physical properties of the device and relating the voltage and current to these physical properties. If this latter approach is to succeed, a great deal must be known about the physics of a device. As such knowledge is not assumed here, this approach will not be used.

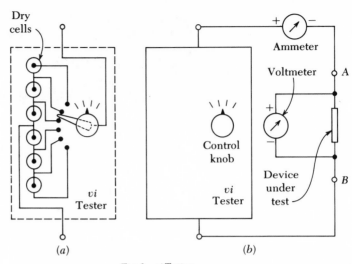

Fig. 1   *vi* Tester

Figure 1*b* shows what we shall call a *voltage-current tester*, an imaginary device that could be constructed in a laboratory. Any sort of current-carrying two-terminal device can be connected between terminals *A* and *B*. The essential features are a center-scale voltmeter, a center-scale ammeter, and a means for varying the voltage—represented in the figure by a knob. What is inside the box with the knob is not really important. It could be a set of dry cells connected to a rotary switch as in Fig. 1*a*.

The details of the operation of the meters are not important now. We assume that the indicator is centered when there is no voltage or current. When an actual current goes through the ammeter from the plus-marked terminal to the other terminal, the indicating needle swings upscale; when the actual current is the other way, the needle swings downscale. The voltmeter operates in a similar fashion. Both meters are assumed to be ideal in the sense that across the ammeter there is zero voltage and through the voltmeter there is zero current. Actual meters approximate this ideal to a high degree.

In making the measurements, the control knob is adjusted to a sequence of positions, and simultaneous readings of the voltage and current are made. The resulting data can be plotted as a graph of voltage against current (or current against voltage). Many different curves will be obtained depending on the device in question.

Three such curves are shown in Fig. 2. The second curve is typical of a device called a *diode*. (Consideration of this device will be deferred until Unit 6.) The third curve is typical of a device called a *tunnel diode*. (We shall not study this device here.)

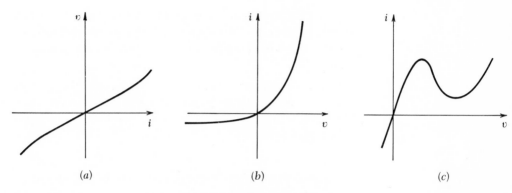

(*a*)	(*b*)	(*c*)

Fig. 2   (In This Figure, *v* and *i*
Are Meter Readings.)

2 APPROXIMATE VOLTAGE-CURRENT CURVE

In this section, we shall give consideration to devices whose voltage-current (abbreviated *vi*) curve resembles that of Fig. 2*a* in the preceding section. A specific curve, with numerical scales, is shown below as a solid line. Note the following about its characteristics:

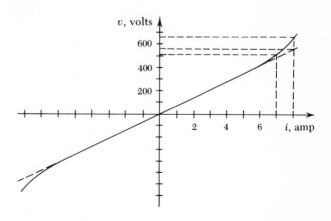

When the current is positive, the sign of the voltage is _______________; when the voltage is negative, the sign of the current is _______________ The slope of the curve is (check one):

positive
negative

(a) Sometimes positive, sometimes negative
(b) Always positive

(b)

The curve is symmetrical about the origin; that is, if the voltage for a certain positive current is 500 volts, the voltage for a negative current having the same magnitude is _______________ volts.

−500

In the diagram, the dashed line is a straight line passing through the origin and tangential to the solid curve there. Using the scales on the axes, the equation of this line is found to be (approximately)

$v =$ _______________

$70i$

Suppose the straight line is used as the vi relationship of this device, instead of the actual curve. At a current of 7 amp, the actual voltage as read from the curve is approximately 510 volts. At the same current, the voltage from the straight line is _______________ volts. The error in voltage, using the straight line instead of the actual curve, is _______________ volts.

490
20

The question arises as to whether this is a large or small error. It is large compared with 10 and quite small compared with 1,000 volts. Compared with the actual voltage at $i = 7$ amp, the error equals approximately _______________ percent. Such an error may or may not be tolerable depending on the application to which the device is to be put.

$\frac{20}{510} \times 100 = 4$

Suppose the range of current to be expected when this device is used is limited to $-8 < i < +8$ amp. Also, suppose a judgement is made that no more than a 10 percent error in the voltage can be tolerated. Find the maximum percentage of error if the straight line is used instead of the actual vi relationship of the device over this current range.

Maximum error: _______________

approximately 15 percent

State whether or not it is permissible to use the straight line instead of the curve and remain within the specified tolerance.

____

Not permissible

3 RESISTORS

If the abscissa and ordinate are x and y, the equation of a straight line is usually written $y = mx + b$. Here the slope of the line equals _____ and the intercept on the y axis equals_____

m

b

When the corresponding coordinates are i and v and the slope of the line is R, the equation of the straight-line approximation of the vi relationship being discussed above is:

_____

v = Ri

The vi relationship of the device under discussion is approximately $v = Ri$ for (check one):

(a)   All currents
(b)   A limited range of currents

(b)

We can *invent* a hypothetical or ideal device (to give it some degree of reality, we often say it "exists" on paper) whose vi relationship is *exactly* the linear equation $v = Ri$ for *all currents*. This is a linear *model* of the device. We call the model an *ideal resistor* (or just *resistor* for short when there is no chance of a misunderstanding) and represent it with the following symbol:

Referring back to the straight-line graph, the quantity R is (check one):

(a)   Always positive
(b)   Can be positive or negative

(a)

The name given to a hypothetical device whose vi relationship is $v = Ri$ is _____. For this device the relationship $v = Ri$ holds exactly for (check one):

(a)   All currents
(b)   A limited range of currents

(ideal) resistor

(a)

The symbol representing a resistor on a circuit diagram is

For a resistor the vi relationship is _____

v = Ri

The quantity R is _____ (positive/negative)

positive

4 REFERENCE ORIENTATIONS

Part of Fig. 1 in Sec. 1, relating to the measurement of voltage and current, is reproduced below. The actual device, whose

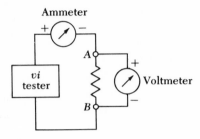

two ends have been labeled A and B, has been replaced by its

(ideal) resistor

model, called _____. The curve relating v and i is also shown below.

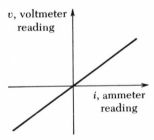

The information given by showing a voltmeter, an ammeter, and a curve relating the simultaneous readings of these two can be supplied by the alternate method of showing reference orientations for the resistor current and voltage and specifying the value of R.

positive

The straight line in the preceding graph is described by $v = Ri$, in which R is _____ (positive/negative). The experimental result previously obtained showed that the voltmeter reading and ammeter reading have the same sign when connected as above. Suppose a voltage reference orientation for the resistor is chosen as shown on the following page. It is desired to choose the current reference orientation in such a way that the combined reference orientations of v and i are consistent with the experimental result; draw the reference arrow for the current.

Suppose the current reference is reversed while the voltage reference is kept the same. Write the resulting expression relating v and i. _____

Of the following four sets of reference orientations for voltage and current of a resistor, there are only two distinctly different combinations. Which pairs are the same?

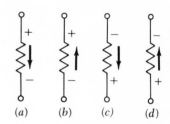

(a)   (b)   (c)   (d)

The two possible choices of reference are as shown below. They can be described as:

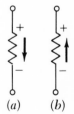

(a)   (b)

(a)   "Voltage reference + sign is at tail of current reference arrow"

(b)   "Voltage reference + sign is at tip of current reference arrow"

Write the vi relations for a resistor for each choice of reference.

Figure (a) _____

Figure (b) _____

5   OHM'S LAW

The linear relationship between v and i in an ideal resistor is called *Ohm's law*. (This is in honor of Georg Ohm who made extensive measurements of the current and voltage of many different metals of different cross-sectional shapes and lengths in the early 1800s.)

If no specification of reference orientations is made, Ohm's law must be written (check one):

(a) $v = Ri$

(b) $|v| = R|i|$

(c)   Neither of these

If Ohm's law is written as $v = Ri$ and no references are shown, it must be assumed that the references are:

(b)

(or both reversed)

(Show the references for v and i.)

The law described by the relationship $v = Ri$ for:

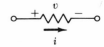

Ohm's law   is called _____

The quantity R (in $v = Ri$), which numerically equals the slope of the line relating v and i, is called the *resistance*. For the linear relationship under consideration, is it true that R is Yes always considered to be positive? _____

The words resis*tor* and resist*ance* have a similar appearance. Match the following in pairs:

(a)   Resistor   (i)   A number

(b)   Resistance   (ii)   An ideal device or mathematical model

(ii)   (a)   and _____

(i)   (b)   and _____

The unit of resistance is the *ohm*, and it is given the symbol Ω (which is the Greek capital omega). If the voltage is in volts and the current is in amperes, the ratio of v to i will be in ohms _____ (units)

For the resistor shown below, suppose $v = 100$ volts when the current is $i = -2$ ma (check one):

(a) The supposition is impossible; because v and i can't have different signs.
(b) The supposition is impossible because current cannot flow from $-$ to $+$.
(c) $R = 50$ kilohms (or 50,000 ohms).
(d) $R = 0.02$ milliohms (or 0.00002 ohms).

In contrast with the current, the voltage is not through the

resistor but _____ it.

Of course, it is possible to invert the expression $v = Ri$ and write $i = v/R$. This is another form of Ohm's law. It is convenient to give the reciprocal of R a name; we call $1/R$ *conductance* and give it the symbol $G = 1/R$. Write Ohm's law using conductance instead of resistance.

$i =$ _____

Conductance is the _____ of resistance. The unit in which G is measured is obtained by spelling backwards

the unit in which R is measured. The unit of G is the _____

If a resist _____ (or/ance) has a resist _____ (or/ance) of 100 ohms, the corresponding G equals _____ (include unit of measure).

In the diagram below, let $R = 100$ kilohms. (How many ohms

is that? _____.) The voltage _____ (through/across) the resistor is $v = 5 \sin 100t$ volts. Find the current in microamperes.

$i =$ _____ μamp.

6   REMARK

We have called the *ideal* device having a linear vi relationship a resistor. But what of an actual physical device, simultaneous measurements of whose voltage and current give an approximate linear relationship—at least over a limited range of current; what should we call it? We shall call it a *physical resistor*, but whenever there is no possibility of confusion, we may abbreviate this merely to resistor. Thus, a *physical resistor* is an actual electrical device; an *ideal resistor* is a hypothetical device (a model) having an exactly *linear* voltage-current relationship.

7   SOURCES (REFERENCE SECTION)

In a resistor, energy is irreversibly transformed from an electrical form to heat. The process is labeled "irreversible" because cooling the resistor, for example, in a refrigerator, will not produce electrical energy.

There are many devices in which energy is reversibly transformed between electrical energy and some other form. In general, these devices are called *sources*. A large part of electrical technology deals with the design of such energy-converting devices. Such designing requires an extensive knowledge of the details of the physical processes whereby the energy is converted. But in this text, we only want to discuss the *use* of these devices in a network. Therefore, we only need the relationship between the voltage and current at the terminals of each device. At this time we shall examine only one type of source—a battery of chemical cells.

Figure 3 shows the previously described *voltage-current tester*, connected to a battery represented on the diagram by a stack of alternate long and short lines. (You may notice that the positions of the ammeter $+$ and $-$ signs are interchanged—compared with the previous application. The only reason for this change is to avoid a minus sign at a later time. There is no fundamental reason in either application for choosing one ammeter connection in preferance to the other. The choice has the same arbitrariness as the choice of a reference orientation.)

As before, simultaneous measurements of the voltage and current at the terminals are made, using the ideal instruments

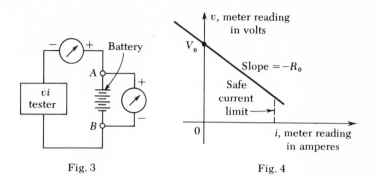

Fig. 3   Fig. 4

earlier described. A plot of v against i gives an approximately straight line as in Fig. 4. Its intercept on the voltage axis is labeled V_0. Let the slope of the line be $-R_0$.

In order to be able to analyze networks that include batteries, two steps are taken, starting with the experimental vi graph.

(a)   Even though there may actually be a slight curvature to the graph, it is often assumed to be a straight line; that is, the vi curve is assumed to be *linear*. This assumption is valid for many applications.

(b)   Suitable "paper network" components are invented to replace the battery.

They are endowed with appropriate properties so that a suitable application of Kirchhoff's laws leads to the same linear relationship as for the battery.

The result of this two-stage process is called a *linear model*. We shall now consider the construction of such a model.

8   LINEAR MODEL OF A BATTERY

Our objective is to develop a linear model for a real, physical battery. From the curve in Fig. 4 of the last section, write an expression relating the v and i of a battery, using the symbols given there.

$V_0 - R_0 i$

$v = $ _____

voltage

The quantity $R_0 i$ has the dimensions of _____. Let $R_0 i$ be temporarily replaced by the symbol v_1, then the preceding equation becomes

$v = V_0 - v_1$

64   OHM'S LAW, SOURCES AND POWER

This is reminiscent of Kirchhoff's voltage law around a loop consisting of _____ (how many?) branches. From the form of the equation, this loop will be as shown below.

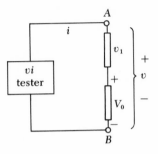

The two boxes have replaced the battery, and, therefore, when we have determined what should be inside each box, these two things taken together will be the *model* of the battery.

The reference + was purposely omitted from v_1. Place a + sign for the reference of v_1 on the diagram, so as to be consistent with the above equation: $v = V_0 - v_1$

The box labeled v_1 has a vi relationship previously established as $v_1 = $ _____

Place a reference arrow for i that will be consistent with the polarity marks on the ammeter in Fig. 3.

The device in the corresponding box must be a _____ and R_0 is its _____. The equation $v_1 = R_0 i$ is an expression of _____ law.

In the diagram below, insert a suitable component in the blank space and label it appropriately.

Considering all possible points on the characteristic vi curve, the quantity v_1, which equals $R_0 i$, _____ (depends/does not depend) on the current i.

three

+ at bottom of v_1

$R_0 i$

(Up from B to A)

resistor
resistance
Ohm's

depends

V_0

independent of

remains constant

Yes; is

is

voltage source

model

Now we shall consider the other box. The terminal voltage of the battery from A to B has been labeled v. When the current is zero, from the vi graph, we find this terminal voltage equals _____. Hence, V_0 is the *open-circuit* terminal voltage of the battery. Its value is _____ (dependent on/independent of) the current i. As the current changes, V_0 _____ (changes/remains constant).

In the preceding diagram, V_0 is the voltage across the lower rectangle. Is it also the voltage across the terminals AB when there is no current? _____. V_0 _____ (is/is not) the open-circuit voltage of the *actual* battery. It _____ (is/is not) the open-circuit voltage of the *model* of the battery.

On the basis of this observation, we shall now *invent* a hypothetical two-terminal device called an *ideal voltage source*, abbreviated *voltage source*, having the property that the voltage across its terminals does not depend on the current flowing through it. We designate a voltage source by a circle, as shown below.

Whenever you see the circle with $\pm$ signs inside, you will know this is a _____. There will also be a letter alongside (usually v or V with some sort of subscript) to represent the voltage of that source. The $\pm$ signs are the reference for that voltage.

Now complete the _____ for the battery by adding suitable labels to the following diagram:

(a) Place a label on the resistor.
(b) Correctly place $\pm$ signs on the source symbol, and place the appropriate voltage symbol next to it.

open-circuit

In the model, R_0 is called the *internal* resistance of the battery; source voltage V_0 is the _____ voltage.

Complete the following statements:

R_0

internal

minus the slope
(of the vi curve)

The resistor in the model has a resistance labeled _____ and called the _____ resistance. Its value (in terms of the original vi graph) is equal to _____

V_0

open-circuit

v-axis intercept
(of the vi curve)

The source voltage is labeled _____ and called the _____ voltage. In terms of the original vi graph, its value equals the _____

9   REVIEW

internal resistance

voltage source

The model of a battery consists of two components: a resistor with resistance R_0 called the _____ and a _____. The latter is a two-terminal device whose voltage is (check one):

(b)

(a)   A linear function of its current

(b)   Independent of its current

nothing

In value, V_0 is the voltage at the terminals of a battery when the terminals have _____ (nothing/a resistance R_0) connected to them.

open-circuit

Consequently, V_0 is the _____ voltage.

Draw and correctly label a model of a storage battery having an internal resistance of $\frac{1}{2}$ ohm and an open-circuit voltage of 6 volts.

$R_0 = 0.5$

$V_0 = 6$

The diagram below shows a voltage source connected to a resistor whose resistance can be varied (as implied by the arrow through it).

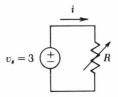

$v_s = 3$

As the current increases, the voltage of the voltage source (check one):

(a) Increases
(b) Stays the same
(c) Decreases

On the accompanying axes, plot the vi relationship of this voltage source.

(b)

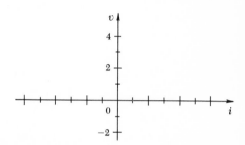

10 MODELS WITH TIME-VARYING VOLTAGE SOURCES

The notion of a hypothetical device called a *voltage source*, having a voltage completely independent of its current, was developed in terms of the terminal vi relationship of a battery. In the case of the model of a battery, the voltage of the voltage source is independent of time as well as of current. There are other generators of electrical energy besides batteries; and many of them are *time-varying*, such as those used to generate the commercial electricity available from power companies, which varies as a sine function of time, as shown on the left below. Similarly, the voltage that causes the "spot" to scan the screen of an oscilloscope varies with time in the shape of a "sawtooth," as shown on the right below.

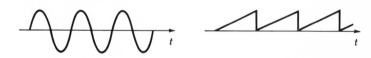

For such a time-varying generator we can also invent a hypothetical device whose voltage changes with *time* but which, *at any given instant*, does not depend on the current flowing through it; that is, it does not depend on what is connected to its terminals. The variation with time is a result of the internal processes of the source, but this variation _____

is not

(is/is not) affected by its terminal current. Such a device is also called a *voltage source* and given the same symbol as before, with some suitable formula to describe how the source voltage varies with time.

The following are claimed to be voltages of voltage sources (see diagram below). State for each whether the claim is true:

(a)   and (c), okay
(b)   No, because v_s
      depends on current

(a) $v_s = 12$ volts
(b) $v_s = 3i$ volts
(c) $v_s = 8e^{-2t}$ volts, for $t > 0$

Actual generators of electricity may approximate (ideal) voltage sources. However, they differ from the ideal by having their terminal voltage somewhat dependent on what is connected to their terminals. The wall socket in a well wired house is almost an ideal voltage source. However, if the wiring is too small, it may be observed that a light operating from the same outlet will dim when some device requiring a lot of current (such as a heater or refrigerator) is turned on. (This phenomenon is similar to the dimming of automobile headlights when the starting motor is activated.) This phenomenon means that the voltage of the wall socket _____

depends

(depends/does not depend) on the current. This wall socket is not a voltage source, because the voltage depends on (check one):

(b)

(a)   Time
(b)   The current

When an actual generator of electrical power cannot be adequately approximated by a voltage source, it can sometimes be represented by a model having the same structure as the

voltage source

model of a battery. This consists of a _____ and a

resistor

_____. Draw such a model in the dashed box below between terminals A and B, and label the components.

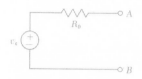

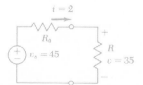

This model can be used both for a battery and for other types of generators. The voltage v_s _____ (might/cannot) be a function of time.

might

Is it possible for the reference orientation of the voltage source in the above model to be the opposite of that chosen?

Yes

11 REVIEW PROBLEMS

Solve each of the following problems, and verify your answers opposite the arrows at the end of each problem. If you need assistance, follow the solution outlined, but only to the extent necessary.

PROBLEM 1

When referring to a battery, it is customary to specify its open-circuit voltage. Thus, a 12-volt automobile battery has an open-circuit voltage of 12 volts.

A 45-volt battery of dry cells is providing a current of 2 amp to an external resistor R across which the voltage is 35 volts. Find the internal resistance R_0 of the battery and the value of the external resistance R.

SOLUTION

As a first step, draw a model of the battery; label the known quantities with their values, and label the unknowns with their symbols.

Using KVL, find the voltage across R_0 and enter its value together with its reference orientation on the diagram below.

R_0

Then, using Ohm's law,

$R_0 =$ _____

$R =$ _____

$R_0 = 5$ ohms

$R = 17.5$ ohms

PROBLEM 2

It is required to find the numerical values in the model of an automobile storage battery. Two voltage measurements are made at the terminals of the battery: (a) with the battery terminals open, the voltage is found to be 12 volts; (b) with a 1-ohm resistor connected to the terminals, the voltage is found to be 11.6 volts. Find the component values R_0, V_0.

SOLUTION

Again it is useful to draw a diagram. From the first of the measurements, the current in the internal resistance equals _____.

This means the voltage across R_0 equals _____ volts.

zero

0

Then, using KVL and the measured voltage,

$V_0 =$ _____

12 volts

What is a name for V_0 that describes it in terms of the terminal condition?

V_0 is the _____ voltage.

open-circuit

Turning to the second measurement, again a diagram will help. Draw a model of the battery and attach a 1-ohm resistor appropriately. From Ohm's law and using the measured value of voltage, find the current in this resistor. (Reference orientation?)

$i =$ _____ amp. What is the value of the current in R_0? _____. From KVL, find the voltage across R_0. $v_{R_0} =$ _____ volts. Finally, from Ohm's law, $R_0 =$ _____ ohms.

11.6

The same, 11.6

0.4

$\dfrac{0.4}{11.6} = 0.0345$

12 BACK TO THE BATTERY

The model of a battery was arrived at from measurements of terminal voltage and current. The voltage was plotted as the ordinate with the current as the abscissa, as repeated here. Suppose the line is now extended beyond the point marked "Safe current limit," in the diagram below, so that it intersects the current axis at the point marked I_0. (This is a geometrical

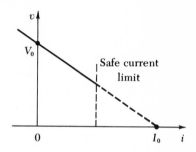

construction, not actually requiring the current to be increased beyond the safe limit.)

R_0

Since the slope of the line has a magnitude equal to _____, this new intercept can be expressed as a function of R_0 and V_0, as

$\dfrac{V_0}{R_0}$

$$I_0 = \underline{\hspace{10cm}}$$

The equation of the line was previously written $v = V_0 - R_0 i$. Rewrite this expression to solve for i in terms of v, and, in the second line, use the previous relationship to introduce I_0.

(a) $\dfrac{V_0}{R_0} - \dfrac{v}{R_0}$

(a) $i =$

(b) $I_0 - \dfrac{v}{R_0}$

(b) $i =$ (in terms of I_0)

0

From the diagram, I_0 is the value the terminal current i would have if $v =$ _____ were possible. This means the terminals of the battery under this condition would be short-circuited. The current I_0 is, consequently, called the _____

short-circuit

_____ current.

Note that I_0 is greater than the safe limit of current for the battery. If an actual battery is short-circuited for an appreciable length of time, it will "run down" and may be irreparably dam-

is not

aged. It _____ (is/is not) appropriate for a real physical battery to think of its short-circuit current. As far as the

can

circuit *model* of a battery is concerned, it _____ (can/cannot) be short-circuited.

The quantity v/R_0, in the equation $i = I_0 - v/R_0$, has the physical dimensions of a _____. Hence, the equation $i = I_0 - v/R_0$ is reminiscent of Kirchhoff's current law applied to a junction at which _____ (how many?) branches are connected. One of these, carrying the current i, is the external branch connected to the battery. From the form of the second term (namely, $-v/R_0$) on the right of the preceding equation, another of the branches is known to be a(an) _____

current

three

(ideal) resistor

The diagram below shows the terminals AB of the battery with an external resistor connected on the right. This is one of the three branches. Complete the diagram, adding references where needed and using a box for the branch carrying I_0; label the branches with appropriate symbols.

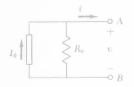

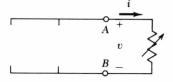

In terms of V_0 and R_0,

$I_0 =$

The quantity I_0 (check one):

(a) Varies with terminal voltage v

(b) Is a constant, independent of v

$\dfrac{V_0}{R_0}$

(b)

13 ALTERNATE MODEL OF BATTERY

When confronted with a similar situation earlier we *invented* a hypothetical device called a voltage source. We shall now invent another hypothetical device whose *current is independent of the voltage at its terminals*. We shall call it an *ideal current source (abbreviated current source)* and give it the symbol

The fact that the symbol is a circle carries the message (as in the case of a voltage source) that it is a source, and the arrow, which gives the reference orientation, denotes that it is a current source.

In the case of a voltage source, what appears on the diagram instead of the arrow? _____

A letter (usually i or I with some sort of subscript) is placed beside the circle to represent the current of the source.

Using this newly introduced symbol complete the diagram below, to arrive at a model of the battery, using appropriate symbols and references for the branches. (Make your references agree with the previous diagram.)

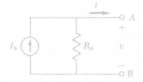

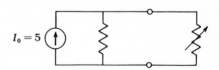

Source current I_0 is called the _____ current. On the graph of the vi relationship of the battery, the quantity I_0 is the _____. The branch labeled R_0 is a _____, and R_0 is called the _____ of the battery. The branch labeled I_0 is a _____. The value I_0 of a current source _____ (may vary with/does not depend on) the voltage across its terminals.

14 MORE ON CURRENT SOURCES

The diagram shows a model of a battery connected to a variable resistor. At a particular setting of the variable resistor,

$$I_0 = 5 \uparrow$$

the source current is $I_0 = 5$. When the resistor setting is changed so as to increase the voltage across it, the value of I_0 (check one):

(a) Increases
(b) Stays the same
(c) Decreases

constant

The circular symbol in the preceding model of a battery carries a current I_0, which is _____ (constant/ varying).   A device having such a property is called a(n)

(ideal) current source

_____

For the battery model developed in the preceding section, the current of the current source is independent of time. The meaning of ideal current source is now extended to include the possibility that its current can be varying with time. The stipulation is that *the current does not depend on the voltage across the source,* even though the current may be changing with time.

Each of the following graphs is claimed to be the current of an ideal current source. Apply this definition, and check those that represent a current source.

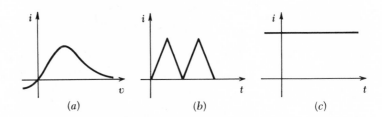

(a)   (b)   (c)

(a)   Not possible

(a) _____

(b)   and (c), okay

(b) _____

(c) _____

15 RELATIONSHIP OF TWO MODELS

We now have two different models for a battery. Draw each of these two models below, label the branches appropriately and complete the expression for the vi relationship under each figure.

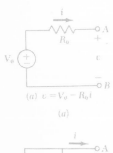

$(a)\ v = V_0 - R_0 i$

(a)

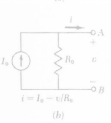

$i = I_0 - v/R_0$

(b)

$(a=)$

i

$\xrightarrow{\quad}$—o A
$+$

v

_____—o B

$v =$

(a)

i

$\xrightarrow{\quad}$—o A
$+$

v

_____—o B

$i =$

(b)

Each of these diagrams is *equivalent* at terminals AB to a battery with a linear vi characteristic, because it (check one):

(a)   Has the same internal resistance
(b)   Has the same terminals
(c)   Has the same vi relationship
(d)   Has the same open-circuit voltage

Describe what to do at the terminals in order to measure V_0 with an ideal instrument.

_____

In each of the two models, there is a resistor. The resistances

are _____ (the same/different).

From a comparison of the two vi relationships, how is R_0

related to I_0 and V_0? $R_0 =$ _____. R_0 is called the

_____ of the battery.

The measured graph of the vi relationship of a battery is shown in the following diagram.

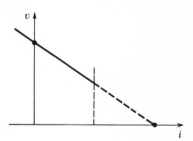

Label the intercepts.

(a) v-axis intercept: _____
(b) i-axis intercept: _____

Is the preceding expression for R_0 consistent with the interpretation of the slope of this line? _____

16   EQUIVALENT CIRCUIT

Since the vi relationship of each model is the same as the linear approximation of the vi graph of the battery, each model will be *equivalent* to the battery; in the sense that if the battery is replaced in a network by its model, no measurement in the remainder of the network can detect the difference, because

the resulting currents and voltages will be the same as they would have been with the battery. For this reason, a model of a physical device is also called an *equivalent circuit* of the device. The term *equivalent circuit* of a physical device
_____ (has/does not have) the same meaning as *model*.

has

Each of the two models of the battery has a vi relationship at its terminals which is the same as the linear approximation of the vi graph of the battery. In this sense, each is _____ to the battery.

equivalent

Is the vi relationship of one model the same as that of the other? _____. Can we say that one of them is an equivalent circuit of the other? _____

Yes
Yes

One of the battery models is equivalent to the other because
_____

they have the same
vi relationships

The idea of equivalence has validity only at the specified terminals at which two devices have the same vi relationship. Nothing can be said about the equality of currents or voltages anywhere inside the devices. More precisely, we say that one *two-terminal device is equivalent to, or is an equivalent circuit of, another one at their terminals if the vi relationships of the two at their terminals are the same.*

In the two models of a battery redrawn below, the first one has a vi relationship at terminals AB of $v = V_0 - R_0 i$. The second one has _____ (the same/a different) vi relationship at AB. The two are equivalent; the current in R_0 in both

the same

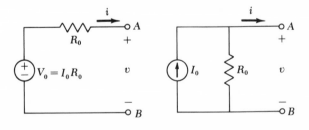

will not necessarily be   diagrams _____
(will be/will not necessarily be) the same under identical terminal conditions.

17   REVIEW PROBLEMS

PROBLEM 1

A model of a battery is shown below.

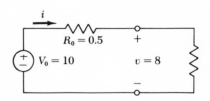

When a certain resistor is connected to the battery, the terminal voltage measures 8 volts. By Ohm's law the current in R_0 is given as a voltage divided by R_0. The appropriate voltage to use is (check one):

(a)   The voltage of the source
(b)   The voltage across R_0

In the above case, the value of i equals (check one):

(a)   20 amp
(b)   4 amp

PROBLEM 2

A 12-volt battery has an internal resistance of 1.5 ohms. Draw a model of the battery which contains a current source. Find the numerical value of each part of the model, and label it appropriately.

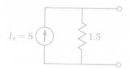

PROBLEM 3

A battery having an internal resistance of 0.8 ohms has a 2-ohm resistor connected across its terminals. The current in this resistor is found to be 5 amp. Find the unknown parts of both models of the battery. (Drawing appropriate diagrams may be helpful.)

(b)

(b)

$I_0 = 8$

$I_0 = 17.5$
$V_0 = R_0 I_0 = 14$

PROBLEM 4

The diagram below shows the *external characteristic* (that is, the terminal vi relationship) of a dc generator. Determine the approximate values of the parameters of two equivalent circuits to represent the generator over the range of current $0 < i < 40$ amp.

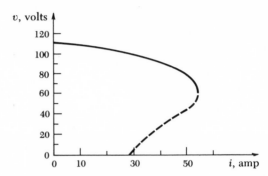

(One possible
set of answers)
$V_0 = 110$ volts
$I_0 = 220$ amp
$R_0 = 0.5$ ohm

PROBLEM 5

A particular combination of a current source, voltage source, and resistor is shown in the diagram below. Apply Kirchhoff's laws and Ohm's law, in order to obtain an equation relating the terminal v and i. Refer to the solution below only if necessary. The answer is opposite the arrow.

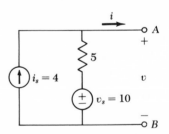

SOLUTION

Let i_5 be the current in the 5-ohm resistor, with reference downward. From KCL at the junction:

$4 - i$

$i_5 = $ _____

Now let v_5 be the voltage across the 5-ohm resistor with ref-

$10 + v_5$

erence + at the top. From KVL, $v = $ _____. Also, v_5 and i_5 are related in a simple way. Write this relationship:

$v_5 = 5i_5$

_____

These three equations combine to give the following vi relationship:

$30 - 5i$

$\longleftarrow$ $v = $ _____ volts

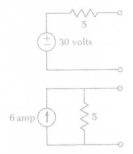

PROBLEM 6
Find two "equivalent circuits" of the network in Prob. 5, that is, networks which have the same vi relationship at their terminals.

By KCL at X:

$i + \dfrac{v - 40}{5} + \dfrac{v}{10} + 10 = 0$

$i = -2 - \dfrac{3}{10}\,v$

PROBLEM 7 (MORE CHALLENGING THAN THE OTHERS)
Apply Kirchhoff's laws and Ohm's law to write the vi relationship of the network below, at terminals AB, expressing i as a function of v. Also find the component values of two equivalent circuits.

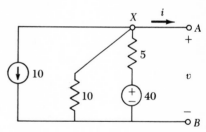

18 VOLTAGE AND ENERGY
The concept of voltage between two points was introduced earlier through a consideration of the work done by an electrostatic field when a charge moves between the two points. Specifically, the voltage from point A to B is the energy expended per unit charge by an electrostatic field when the

A; B

charge moves from _____ to _____.
If work is done by the field as the charge moves, the potential

decrease

energy will _____ (increase/decrease).

Now, instead of a single charge, suppose there is a stream of positive charges moving from A to B through a branch that is part of a network (see diagram below). The branch is not necessarily a resistor or battery but may be some other device or combination of devices. The voltage and current reference orientations are as shown.

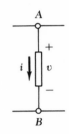

If a positive charge moves through a branch from one point to another of lower potential, the electrostatic field has expended energy. This energy is *delivered to* the branch, where it is transformed to some other form: changed to heat, stored as chemical energy (as in a battery), stored as magnetic energy, etc.

If the positive charge moves in a branch from a point of lower to a point of higher potential, the branch will, instead, be delivering energy *to* the electrostatic field.

Suppose that a total positive charge of $q = 3$ coul goes through the branch from A to B in 2 sec. How much energy would be expended by the electrostatic field? $W_{AB} =$ _____ joules. What is the average current during this time? _____ (include unit of measure).

$3v$ joules

$\dfrac{3}{2}$ amp

Now suppose the charge moving from A to B is infinitesimal, say Δq, and the time it takes for it to go from A to B is Δt. The voltage is still v. The energy expended by the electrostatic field will be

$v\,\Delta q$

$\dfrac{\Delta q}{\Delta t}$

$\Delta W_{AB} =$ _____

During the interval Δt the *average current* equals _____

If the previous expression for the energy expended is divided by Δt, we get

$$\frac{\Delta W_{AB}}{\Delta t} = v\,\frac{\Delta q}{\Delta t}$$

$\frac{dq}{dt}$

current

dW_{AB}/dt

i

energy

voltage; current

Finally, let Δt approach zero. Then $\Delta q/\Delta t$ becomes the derivative, written _____ . But this derivative is the rate at which charge is moving from A to B, which is a quantity called the _____

Similarly $\Delta W_{AB}/\Delta t$, becomes a derivative written _____ . This is the rate at which energy is being expended by the electrostatic field. When all of the preceding is combined, the result is

$$\frac{dW_{AB}}{dt} = v(\quad)$$

In words, this expression states that the rate at which _____ is being expended by the electrostatic field, when a current flows between two points across which the voltage is v, is given by the product of _____ and _____

19 POWER AND ENERGY

The term *power* is defined as the *rate of transfer of energy*, or the *rate of doing work:* Here, we shall be careful to specify the *sense* of the energy transfer; that is, whether the energy is being expended *by* the electrostatic field and being transferred to the branch, or the opposite.We shall define *power delivered to* a branch as the rate at which energy is expended *by* the electrostatic field. It will be represented by p. As a derivative,

$\frac{dW_{AB}}{dt}$

$p = vi$

$p = $ _____

Hence, the previous expression $dW_{AB}/dt = vi$ becomes: _____

The branch is redrawn below to focus on the particular references for v and i for which the expression $p = vi$ applies.

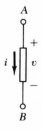

tail

The voltage reference plus is at the _____ (tail/tip) of the current reference arrow.

$p = vi$ is a fundamental expression relating power to voltage and current. The unit of power is the *watt*. From the definition of power as the rate of energy expenditure, 1 watt = 1 _____ (nonelectrical unit). In terms of the units of voltage and current, 1 watt = 1 _____

joule/sec

volt-amp

If a positive charge moves from one point to another point which is actually at a lower potential, the power will be _____ (positive/negative)

positive

In the diagram below, suppose i and v are simultaneously positive. The power actually delivered to the branch will

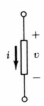

be _____ (positive/negative) at that time. At another time, suppose v is numerically negative while i is positive. The power delivered to the branch will be _____ (positive/negative).

positive

negative

The power p delivered to (or absorbed by) a branch can be either positive or negative. If p is negative, this means that power is actually _____ (delivered to/supplied by) the branch.

supplied by

The expression $p = vi$ refers to the power delivered to a branch for a particular set of reference orientations for v and i. Show them on the following branch.

For the following references:

the expression for the power delivered to the branch in terms of v and i is

$-vi$

$$p = \underline{\hspace{8cm}}$$

With these references, the actual values of v and i (check one):

(c)

(references are arbitrary)

(a) Must both be negative

(b) Must have opposite signs

(c) Can be either positive or negative

At a particular time, the values of v and i in the branch shown below are $v = 10$ volts, $i = -3$ amp. The expression for p in

$+vi$

terms of v and i is $p = \underline{\hspace{3cm}}$ (show sign also). The numerical value of the electrical power delivered to the

-30 watts

branch equals $\underline{\hspace{3cm}}$ (include unit of measure).

The expression for power delivered to a branch, in terms of the current and voltage of the branch (check one):

(b)

(a) Must always be $p = vi$

(b) Can be $p = +vi$ or $-vi$ depending on the references for v and i

If $p = vi$, the numerical value of p (check one):

(b)

(a) Must be positive

(b) Can be either positive or negative

If $p = -vi$, the numerical value of p (check one):

(c)

(a) Must be positive

(b) Must be negative

(c) Can be either positive or negative

20 POWER FLOW

As current flows through a branch, we refer to the branch as either *absorbing* or *delivering* power. The power *absorbed by* a branch is the same as the power *delivered to* the branch,

p

represented by the symbol $\underline{\hspace{6cm}}$

can

The power absorbed by a branch $\underline{\hspace{3cm}}$ (can/cannot) be either positive or negative. If the branch is actually supplying power, the power being absorbed by that branch will be (check one):

(c)

(a)   Positive

(b)   Nonexistent

(c)   Negative

The diagram below shows two branches connected together.

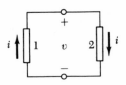

For emphasis, two reference arrows are shown for current i, one beside each branch. Both arrows have the same orientation along the path. Let p_1 and p_2 be the power *delivered to* branches 1 and 2, respectively. In terms of v and i, which may be constant or may vary with time,

(a) $-vi$

(b) $+vi$

(a) $p_1 =$ _____

(b) $p_2 =$ _____

positive

When v and i are numerically positive, p_2 is _____ (positive/negative). Then power is actually being delivered

to

_____ (to/by) branch 2.

In common terminology, a branch to which power is actually being delivered is called a *load*. When v and i are positive,

is

branch 2 above _____ (is/is not) a load. When the v and i references of a branch are such that $p = vi$, and the values of v and i are such that p is positive, the branch is a

load

_____

For convenience, the set of v and i references for which $p = +vi$ is called a set of *load references*. Referring back to the diagram, for a set of load references, the voltage reference $+$

tail

sign is located at the _____ (tip/tail) of the current reference arrow.

For each of the branches below, add the missing reference to make the set a load set of references.

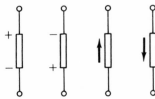

If a given branch is to be a load (check one):

(b)

(a)   The references of v and i must constitute a load set of references.

(b)   The power delivered to the branch must be positive.

are

In the diagram below, the references _____ (are/are not) a load set. Suppose that at some time $v = 50$ and

is not

$i = -2$. Under these conditions, the branch _____ (is/is not) a load.

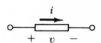

If a branch has a set of load references, it is (check one):

(b)

(a)   Always a load

(b)   A load only when the product vi is positive

(c)   A load only when v and i are each positive

The previous diagram is redrawn below. We have discussed branch 2; now focus on branch 1. In terms of v and i, the power

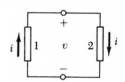

to branch 1 is:

$-vi$

$p_1 = $ _____

negative

If v and i are positive, p_1 is _____ (positive/neg-

by

ative). Then power is actually being delivered _____ (to/by) branch 1. When a branch is actually delivering power, it is commonly called a *source* branch. Under the above con-

source

ditions, branch 1 is a _____ (source/load) branch.

Again for convenience, the v and i references for which $p = -vi$ are called *source* references. Place a set of source references on the following branch.

or

For the following diagram, list those branches that have load references and those that have source references.

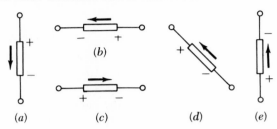

(a) (b) (c) (d) (e)

Source: _____

Load: _____

A certain branch has source references for v and i, and the vi product is negative. This branch is acting as a _____ (load/source).

For the load set of references, vi is the power delivered _____ (to/by) the branch, in an algebraic sense. If vi is positive, the branch is actually _____ (absorbing/supplying) power; if vi is negative, the branch is actually _____ (absorbing/supplying) power.

The choice of which set of references to use on a branch (check one):

(a) Is arbitrary
(b) Depends on knowing whether the branch is supplying or absorbing power

Suppose that the numerical values of the voltage and current of a branch are known and that it is desired to find the numerical value of the power p into the branch. The first step is to determine whether the appropriate expression relating p to v and i is $p = +vi$ or $p = -vi$. Then, the numerical values can be inserted. In the diagram below, the references _____ (are/are not) the load set; so, in terms of v and i, $p = $ _____. The numerical value of p is $p = $ _____ (include unit of measure). The branch is actually _____ (absorbing/supplying) power.

$i = 6$

$v = -10$

For each of the branches shown below, find the numerical value of the power p *into* the branch (in watts) and state whether the branch is actually absorbing or supplying power.

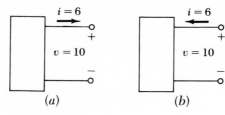

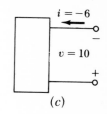

(a)   (b)   (c)

(a) $p = -60$; supplying   (a) _____

(b) $p = 60$; absorbing   (b) _____

(c) $p = 60$; absorbing   (c) _____

21 INSTANTANEOUS POWER

In the numerical examples of the preceding discussion, v and i in the expression $p = vi$ were constants. To emphasize that v and i can be time dependent, we write

$$p(t) = v(t)i(t)$$

The power at any given instant is the product of voltage and current at that instant.

Suppose, for a branch with load references, that $v = 5t$ and $i = (t-2)$. Write an expression for the rate at which energy is absorbed in the branch.

$p = 5t(t-2)$

$p =$ _____

Sometimes, the formula for v or i as a function of time t is different over different ranges of t. In such cases, the formula for p will be different over the various ranges of t.

Suppose $v = 10$ volts and i is given by the graph shown below. Write formulas for $i(t)$ over the following ranges of t:

(a) $i(t) = 4t$ (a) $i(t) =$ _____ $0 \leqslant t \leqslant 1$

(b) $i(t) = 8-4t$ (b) $i(t) =$ _____ $1 \leqslant t \leqslant 2$

(c) $i(t) = 0$ (c) $i(t) =$ _____ $t > 2$

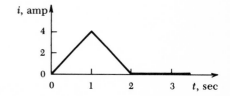

For these same ranges, write expressions for $p(t)$:

(a) $p(t) = 40t$

(b) $p(t) = 80 - 40t$

(c) $p(t) = 0$

(a) $p(t) =$ _____

(b) $p(t) =$ _____

(c) $p(t) =$ _____

Find expressions for the power delivered to a branch for all $t > 0$, if v and i have load references and are given by the graphs below.

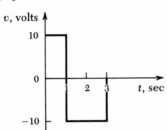

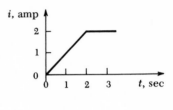

(a)

$v = 10$

$i = t$

$p = 10t$

(b)

$v = -10$

$i = t$

$p = -10t$

(c)

$v = -10$

$i = 2$

$p = -20$

(d)

$p = 0$

(a) $0 < t < 1$

$v =$

$i =$

$p =$

(b) $1 < t < 2$

$v =$

$i =$

$p =$

(c) $2 < t < 3$

$v =$

$i =$

$p =$

(d) $t > 3$

$p =$

Sketch the curve of p against t on the axes given. Label the axes with scale values.

(Not to same scale)

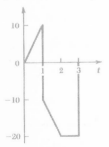

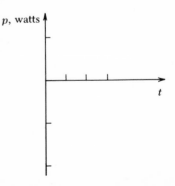

During what interval of t will this branch be actually delivering power? _____

1 to 3

22   OBTAINING ENERGY FROM POWER

The power absorbed by a branch is the rate at which energy is absorbed. That is,

$$p = \frac{dW}{dt}$$

(The subscripts AB have been omitted for simplicity.) If an expression for p is known, W can be obtained from p by the mathematical operation of _____ with respect to _____ (name of variable).

integration

time

In the following diagram, the numerical values are valid for $t = 0$ to 5 sec.

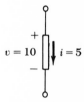

$v = 10$ $i = 5$

$p = vi = 50$

How much energy is absorbed in the branch during this time?

$W =$ (include unit of measure)

$W = \int_0^5 50 \, dt = 250$ joules

Suppose $p = 5t(t-2)$ watts. Find the energy absorbed by the branch from $t = 2$ to 5 sec.

$W =$ (include unit of measure)

$W = \int_2^5 5t(t-2) \, dt$

$= \left(\frac{5t^3}{3} - 5t^2 \right) \Big|_2^5$

$= 90$ joules

If the expression for $p(t)$ is not the same for all values of t, the integration over different intervals must be carried out using the appropriate expression for p in each interval.

Suppose p is given by the curve shown.

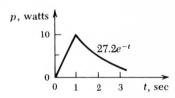

p, watts

$27.2e^{-t}$

Expressions for p (in watts) are:

$p(t) = 10t$ for $0 \leq t \leq 1$

$p(t) = 27.2e^{-t}$ for $1 \leq t$

The energy from, say, $t = 0$ to 3 is

$$W = \int_0^3 p(t)\ dt = \int_0^1 10t\ dt + \int_1^3 27.2e^{-t} dt$$
$$= 5 + 27.2e^{-1} - 27.2e^{-3} = 13.65 \text{ joules}$$

Suppose in this example it is desired to find the energy over all time. This energy is:

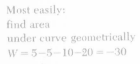

$$W = \underline{\hspace{3cm}} \text{ joules}$$

Let p be given by the example at the end of the last section (see the diagram below), namely,

$$p = \begin{cases} 10t & 0 < t < 1 \\ -10t & 1 < t \leq 2 \\ -20 & 2 \leq t < 3 \\ 0 & 3 < t \end{cases}$$

Find the energy from $t = 0$ to $t = 5$ sec.

Most easily:
find area
under curve geometrically
$W = 5 - 5 - 10 - 20 = -30$

More formally:

$W = \int_0^1 10t\ dt + \int_1^2 -10t\ dt$

$\qquad\qquad + \int_2^3 -20\ dt$

$= 5t^2 \Big|_0^1 - 5t^2 \Big|_1^2 - 20t \Big|_2^3$

$= -30 \text{ joules}$

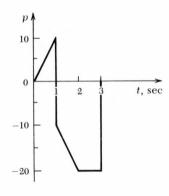

23 POWER ABSORBED BY RESISTORS

In the preceding discussion of power and energy, the nature of the branch that is absorbing or supplying power was not specified. We shall now consider the power absorbed by a resistor.

The diagram below shows a resistor connected to a network represented by the box.

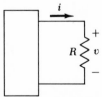

load

+

Ri

Ri^2

The voltage and current reference orientations are also shown; they are the _____ set of references. The power absorbed by the resistor is $p =$ _____ $(+/-)$ vi. But in a resistor, v in terms of i is $v =$ _____. Hence, the expression for power in terms of i is $p =$ _____

$-vi$

$-Ri$

Ri^2

Suppose the reference orientation of v or i (but not both) is reversed. The new expression for the power absorbed by R, in terms of v and i, will be $p =$ _____. The expression for Ohm's law is $v =$ _____. Finally, in terms of i, the expression for p is $p =$ _____. Compare this with the previous expression for load references and state whether the following is true or false.

True

"The power absorbed by a resistor is given by $p = Ri^2$ no matter what references are chosen for v and i." _____

$i = \dfrac{v}{R} = 0.1 \cos 2t$

A 1,000-ohm resistor is connected to a voltage source whose voltage equals $100 \cos 2t$ volts. Find an expression for the power absorbed by the resistor.

$p = Ri^2$

  $= 1.000\ (0.01 \cos^2 2t)$

  $= 10 \cos^2 2t$

$p =$ _____

$\dfrac{v^2}{R}$

Gv^2

The expression $p = Ri^2$ was obtained by substituting for v in the equation $p = vi$. An alternate expression for p can be obtained if i is eliminated instead of v from $p = vi$. In terms of v and R, the expression is $p =$ _____

In terms of the conductance G, this becomes $p =$ _____

Use this equation to find the expression for p in the above example of the 1,000-ohm resistor connected to the voltage source having $v = 100 \cos 2t$.

$0.001\ (100 \cos 2t)^2 = 10$

     $\cos^2 2t$

$p =$ _____

The power absorbed by a resistor can be written in a number of ways:

(a) vi

(b) Ri^2

(c) Gv^2

(a)   In terms of v and i (with load references), $p =$ _____
(b)   In terms of R and i, $p =$ _____
(c)   In terms of G and v, $p =$ _____

Power is the rate at which energy is absorbed. The energy transferred from t_1 to t_2 is given in terms of p as

$\displaystyle\int_{t_1}^{t_2} p\ dt$

$W =$

$$\int_{t_1}^{t_2} Ri^2 \, dt$$

No; cannot

(b)

(a)

Let the energy absorbed by a resistor be labeled W_R. An expression for this energy, over a time interval from t_1 to t_2 when the current in the resistor R is i, will be

$W_R =$ _____

When i is any conceivable function of t, can this quantity ever be negative? _____. A resistor _____ (can/cannot) supply energy.

In the expression $p = v^2/R$ for the power absorbed by a resistor, the voltage v always represents (check one):

(a)   The voltage of a source in the network to which the resistor is connected
(b)   The voltage across the resistor

The diagram below shows a resistor R connected to a battery which is represented by one of its models. In the expression $p = v^2/R$ for the power delivered to R, the value of voltage to use is (check one):

(a)   5 volts
(b)   6 volts

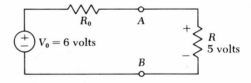

24   REVIEW PROBLEMS

PROBLEM 1
The current in a 500-ohm resistor is given by the graph shown below. Find the energy dissipated by the resistor over the period of time that the current is on (include unit of measure).

$$i = 0.2(t - 1) \qquad 0 < t < 2$$
$$= 0.2 \qquad\qquad 2 < t < 5$$

$$W_R = \int_0^5 500 \, i^2 \, dt$$

$$= \int_0^2 20(t-1)^2 \, dt + \int_2^5 20 \, dt$$

$$= 73.3 \text{ joules}$$

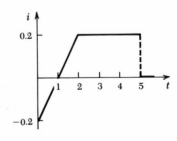

PROBLEM 2

A 2-ohm resistor is connected across a 10-volt battery having internal resistance R_0, as shown below. The voltage across the 2-ohm resistor measures 9 volts.

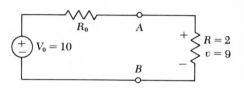

(a) p supplied by $V_0 = V_0$ times i with reference to the right. By Ohm's law: $i = \dfrac{9}{2}$

$\therefore p = 10\left(\dfrac{9}{2}\right) = 45$ watts

(a) Determine the power supplied by the voltage source V_0.

(b) Voltage across R_0 $= 10 - 9 = 1.$ By Ohm's law:

$R_0 = \dfrac{1}{i} = \dfrac{2}{9}$ ohm

(b) Determine the value of R_0.

(c) $p_{R_0} = \dfrac{2}{9}\left(\dfrac{9}{2}\right)^2 = 4.5$ watts

(c) Find the power dissipated in R_0.

(d) $p_R = 2\left(\dfrac{9}{2}\right)^2 = 40.5$ watts

(d) Find the power dissipated in R.

(e) $45 = 4.5 + 40.5$ It is by mine!

(e) By the law of the conservation of energy, you would expect that the power supplied by the source would equal the power dissipated in the two resistors. Is this confirmed by your calculations? _____

PROBLEM 3

Someone with a creative bent decided to put together the network shown below. Each source may be actually delivering power or absorbing power.

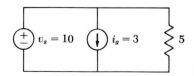

(a)   Find the power dissipated in the resistor.

(b)   Find the power actually supplied or absorbed by the current source; specify which it is.

(c)   Repeat the above for the voltage source.

If you need help, continue to read below. Answers are given opposite the arrows.

SOLUTION

Does the voltage of a voltage source depend on what is connected to its terminals? _____. So the voltage across the resistor (with reference + at top) equals _____ volts. By Ohm's law the resistor current (assuming a load set of references) equals _____ amp _____ (up/down). Then p_R = _____ watts.

Assuming a source set of references for the current source, its voltage equals _____ volts. The expression for the power *supplied by* the current source in terms of v_s and i_g is p = _____; numerically, it is p = _____ watts. The current source actually _____ (supplies/absorbs) power.

Assume a source set of references for the voltage source. By KCL, its current equals _____ amp _____ (up/down). The expression for the power *supplied by* the voltage source, in terms of v_s and i_g is p = _____; numerically, it is p = _____ watts. The voltage source actually _____ (supplies/absorbs) power.

No

10

$\dfrac{10}{5} = 2$; down

$5(2)^2 = 20$ ⟵

$- v_s = - 10$

$-v_s i_g$; -30 ⟵

absorbs   ⟵

$i_g + \dfrac{v_s}{5} = 5$;   up

$v_s \left(i_g + \dfrac{v_s}{5} \right)$

50   ⟵

supplies   ⟵

Resistive Networks

1 INTRODUCTION

Generally speaking, engineers and scientists perform two different kinds of work: (a) *analysis*, or the examination of a whole structure in order to understand its parts and their relationships; and (b) *synthesis* or *design*, or the combination of separate parts into a whole whose characteristics, which are presumably desirable, have been prescribed beforehand.

Many of the problems that an engineer is called upon to solve involve finding either the voltage across, the current through, or the power absorbed by an electrical device when the device is connected in a network of other devices and electrical sources of energy. This is a problem of *analysis.* Conversely, an engineer may be asked to specify the characteristics of one electrical device in a network of other devices, or the amount of power a given source is required to deliver, in order that the voltage, current, or power absorbed somewhere in the network be equal to a specified value. This is a problem of *synthesis* or *design.*

In the preceding units, three hypothetical devices (models) and several laws were introduced. The devices are an ideal resistor, an ideal voltage source, and an ideal current source. (We shall often designate sources as v source or i source.) The laws that describe the interrelations of voltage and current in a network containing these three models are Kirchhoff's laws and Ohm's law. Now, if the behavior of real, physical devices in a network can be adequately represented by combinations of these models, the result will be a network of resistors, v sources, and i sources to which we can apply Kirchhoff's and Ohm's laws.

In this unit, we shall discuss methods leading to the successful solution of problems of analysis and design, involving networks containing only resistors, voltage sources, and current sources. Specifically, by the end of this unit you should be able to do the following:

(a)   Find the voltages and/or currents and/or power absorbed in one or more branches of a network, or the power delivered by one or more sources, when given a network of moderate complexity (say, up to 4 junctions or 10 branches) containing resistors, v sources, and i sources, whose values are specified (*analysis*).

(b)   Find the values of unspecified resistances or sources, when given a network (similar in complexity to the above) in which appropriate branch voltages, currents, or powers are specified (*synthesis* or *design*).

(c)   Do both of the above by any of the following methods:

(i)   Reduction of a given network to an equivalent, more simple network

(ii)   Alternate application of KVL and KCL and Ohm's law

(iii)   Systematic application of KVL, KCL, and Ohm's law in a specific manner, resulting in a set of "loop" equations involving only current variables

(iv)   Systematic application of KCL, KVL, and Ohm's law in an alternate way, resulting in a set of "node" equations involving only voltage variables

2   SERIES CIRCUIT

The diagram on the next page portrays a dry cell connected to a (physical) resistor. A linear model is also shown. Here the battery is replaced by its _____ equivalent, consisting of a voltage source together with the internal resistance R_0. The resistance of the connecting wires is not considered to be negligible and is included in the model as R_w.

voltage source

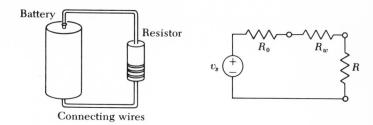

Battery

Resistor

Connecting wires

R_0 R_w

v_s R

The ideal components in the model form a closed loop in which current can flow. Observe how the actual currents in the components must be related to each other. They must be _____

the same or equal

Branches of a network that are connected end-to-end so that they carry the same current (when there is a current) are said to be in *series*. In the above model, the resistors R, R_w, and R_0 are connected _____

in series

In the following diagrams, indicate those in which all components are (and are not) in series.

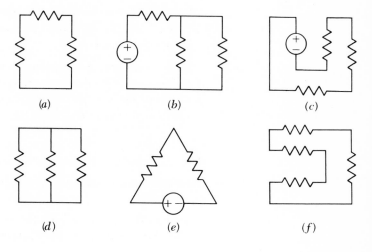

(a) (b) (c)

(d) (e) (f)

(a) In series:
(a); (c); (e); (f)

(b) Not in series:
(b); (d)

(a) In series: _____

(b) Not in series: _____

Yes

The previous battery-resistor model is redrawn on page 98. A current reference is also shown. Is the voltage source in series with the resistors? _____. Let v_{R_0}, v_{R_w}, and v_R be the voltages across the resistors. Select load references for these and write KVL around the loop in terms of these voltages:

$$v_s = v_{R_0} + v_{R_w} + v_R$$

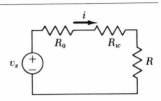

Now we shall use Ohm's law to replace each resistor voltage by a function of current. The result will be

$$R_0 i + R_w i + \underline{\hspace{1cm}} = v_s$$

or

$$(R_0 + R_w + R)i = v_s$$

Ri

The form of this equation is the same as that for a single resistor, namely, resistance times current $= v$. We conclude that a *series connection of resistors can be replaced by a single equivalent resistor whose resistance equals the sum of the series resistances.*

Suppose that in the preceding diagram $R_0 = 0.2$ ohm, $R_w = 0.1$ ohm, and $R = 2$ ohms. What would be the value of the equivalent resistance R_e? _____

2.3 ohms

Four resistors whose resistances are 800 ohms, 1.5 kilohms, 4 kilohms, and 700 ohms are connected in series. Draw a diagram showing this connection, and find the value of the equivalent resistance R.

800   1,500

R —

4,000   700

$R = 7,000 = 7$ kilohms

$R =$ _____

Does the order in which the resistors are connected influence the result? _____

No

Sources in series can also be combined to yield a single source. For example, in the diagram shown below KVL gives

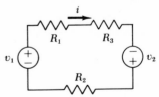

$$v_1 + v_2 = R_1 i + R_2 i + R_3 i$$

In the following simplified diagram, find expressions for v_e and R_e in order for the current to be the same as in the original diagram.

(a) $v_e = v_1 + v_2$
(b) $R_e = R_1 + R_2 + R_3$

(a) $v_e =$ _____

(b) $R_e =$ _____

The diagram to the right below is to be equivalent to the one on the left below. Specify a reference for the voltage source, and express v in terms of v_1 and v_2.

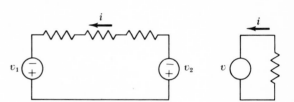

3 PRACTICAL EXAMPLE

The diagram below shows a battery being charged by a battery charger connected through a variable resistor R_3, which serves to provide adjustment of the amount of charging current.

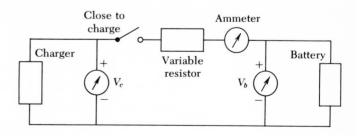

A model of this arrangement is shown below.

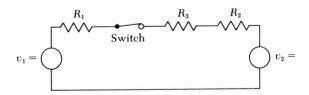

The following measurements are made:

(a) *With the switch open:*
    Voltmeter V_c indicates 18 volts
    Voltmeter V_b indicates 12 volts
    Ammeter indicates _____ amp

      Select references for v_1 and v_2 and determine their values for these references. _____

0

With reference + on top: $v_1 = 18$; $v_2 = 12$. (Change sign if a reference is reversed.)

Place the results on the diagram.

(b) *With the switch closed:*
    Voltmeter V_c indicates 15 volts
    Voltmeter V_b indicates 13.5 volts
    Ammeter indicates 30 amp

      Use KVL to express the voltmeter readings in terms of the quantities shown in the diagram of the equivalent circuit; from these, find the values of R_1 and R_2.

$R_1 = \dfrac{18 - 15}{30} = 0.1$

$R_1 = $ _____ ohm

$R_2 = \dfrac{13.5 - 12}{30} = 0.05$

$R_2 = $ _____ ohm

Ohm's

In this last step, the relationship used is _____ law.

In the preceding diagram, R_3 is still unknown. Reduce the rest of the diagram to a series connection of a voltage source and a resistor. Attach the result to the resistor R_3 shown on the following page and label with numerical values.

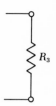

From this circuit, determine the value of R_3 necessary to give the charging current a value of 20 amp.

0.15

$R_3 =$ _____

As R_3 is changed, the current will change. For what value of R_3 will the current have the maximum possible value? $R_3 =$

0

40

_____ ohms. The value of this maximum current is _____ amp.

Suppose $R_3 = 0.25$ ohm, and $v_2 = 20$ volts, all other parameters remaining the same. The value of i is now

−5

$i =$ _____ amp

discharging

The battery is _____ (charging/discharging).

4   VOLTAGE DIVIDER

The diagram below shows two resistors connected in series.

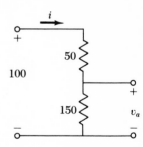

across

Suppose the voltage _____ (across/through) the combination is known to be 100 volts. The voltage v_a across the 150-ohm resistor is to be found.

Suppose the current i is known. Express v_a in terms of i.

150i

$v_a =$ _____

You also know how to find the current in a series circuit. In

$\dfrac{100}{50 + 150} = 0.5$

this circuit, numerically, $i =$ _____ amp. Hence,

150 (0.5) = 75

v_a has the numerical value $v_a =$ _____ volts.

This particular structure occurs very often; that is, the voltage across the series combination of two resistors will be known and it will be desired to find the voltage across one of the two resistors. This is illustrated in the diagram below. A formula

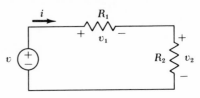

can be derived. First calculate the current i and then use $v_2 = R_2 i$. Thus, to find v_2, we write

$$v_2 = R_2 i = R_2 \frac{v}{R_1 + R_2}$$

or

$$v_2 = \frac{R_2}{R_1 + R_2} v$$

Use the same approach to find an expression for v_1.

$\dfrac{R_1}{R_1 + R_2} v$

$v_1 = $ _____

We observe that the voltage v is *divided* (distributed) between the two resistors. For this reason, the structure has acquired the name *voltage divider*.

In a voltage divider, suppose R_2 is greater than R_1. Then the voltage across R_1 will be _____ (greater/smaller) than the voltage across R_2.

smaller

The *voltage-divider formula* can be stated as follows.

The voltage across one resistor is to the total voltage as the value of that resistance is to the total resistance.

Use this doggerel (rather than first computing the current) to give an expression for v_b in the following diagram.

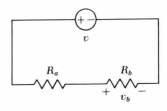

$$\frac{v_b}{v} = \frac{R_b}{R_a + R_b}$$

$$v_b = \frac{R_b}{R_a + R_b} v$$

$$\frac{v_b}{v} = \underline{\hspace{6cm}}$$

$$v_b = \underline{\hspace{6cm}}$$

A 10-ohm resistor is connected to the terminals of a 12-volt battery having an internal resistance of 0.2 ohm. The voltage

$$\frac{10}{10.2}(12) = \frac{120}{10.2} = 11.76$$

across the 10-ohm resistor will be _____ volts.

A *square-wave generator* is a piece of laboratory equipment which can be represented by the model below.

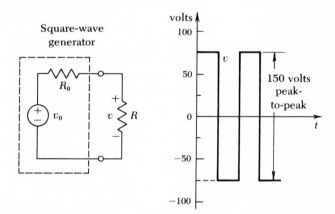

By the voltage-divider formula:

$$v = \frac{R}{R + R_0} v_0$$

or

$$v_0 = \frac{R + R_0}{R} v = \frac{4}{3} v$$

$$\frac{4}{3}(150) = 200$$

(v_0 should be a square wave going from -100 to $+100$ volts.)

The internal resistance R_0 of a particular generator was found to be 100 ohms. A 300-ohm resistor R was connected across the terminals of the generator, and the voltage $v(t)$ across this resistor was observed to be the square wave shown above, having a *peak-to-peak* voltage of 150 volts. The peak-to-peak value of $v_0(t)$ equals _____

Sketch the graph of $v_0(t)$ on the above set of axes.

Measuring the open-circuit voltage of a battery is a simple matter. However, an attempt to measure the short-circuit current directly by short-circuiting the battery terminals can possibly result in ruining the battery, or may alter its characteristics. The alternative is to measure V_0 and the terminal voltage with a known resistance connected. The short-circuit current of the circuit model is then readily computed.

When a 7-ohm resistor is connected to a certain 45-volt battery (see diagram below), the voltage across it measures 42

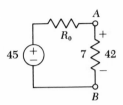

By the voltage-divider formula:

$$\frac{42}{45} = \frac{7}{R_0 + 7}$$

or

(a) $R_0 + 7 = 7 \left(\frac{45}{42}\right) = 7.5$

$R_0 = 0.5$ ohm

(b) $I_0 = \frac{45}{0.5} = 90$ amp

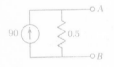

volts. Use the voltage-divider concept to determine the value R_0, and, from this, find the source current I_0 of the current-source equivalent model of a battery. Draw and label the current-source equivalent model.

(a) $R_0 = $ _____

(b) $I_0 = $ _____

5   POWER DELIVERED BY A SOURCE

A certain physical generator is represented by an equivalent circuit consisting of a voltage source in series with a resistor, as shown within the dashed box below. The resistance R represents a load.

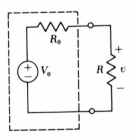

$\frac{v^2}{R}$

In terms of v, the power delivered to resistor R is $p = $ _____.

In a particular case, where $V_0 = 20$ and $R_0 = 1$, use the voltage-divider formula to substitute for v and obtain an expression for p in terms of R only.

$\dfrac{1}{R}\left(\dfrac{20R}{R+1}\right)^2 = \dfrac{400R}{(R+1)^2}$

$p =$ _____

A graph of the function of p against R is shown plotted below.

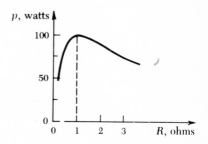

We observe from the curve that the power changes with the value of R and that it reaches a maximum when $R =$ _____

1

It is possible to find the extreme points (maxima or minima) of a function mathematically by (what process?) _____

Setting the derivative equal to zero

An expression for p when $V_0 = 20$ and $R_0 = 1$ was found above. By repeating the same process using general values, the formula for p will be found to be

$$p = \frac{V_0^2\, R}{(R + R_0)^2}$$

(Verify this.) For a given generator, some of the quantities *on the right* are fixed and others are variable. List the fixed and variable quantities.

(a) R_0, V_0

(b) R

(a) Fixed: _____

(b) Variable: _____

Mathematically, find the value of R at which p is a maximum.

R_0

$R =$ _____

Find an expression for the maximum power

$$\frac{V_0^2 R_0}{(R_0 + R_0)^2} = \frac{V_0^2}{4R_0}$$

$P_m =$ _____

Let $R_0 = 1$ and $V_0 = 20$. Find the maximum power and verify it on the above curve.

100

$P_m =$ _____ watts

Consider a certain laboratory power supply which can be represented by a 400-volt voltage source in series with a 100-ohm resistor. It is to supply power to a resistor R. The maximum power will be delivered to R from this arrangement when $R =$ _____. The amount of power will equal

100 ohms

400 watts

_____

In the following diagram, suppose R_2 is to be adjusted so that the maximum possible power is delivered to it. Call this power P_m. When R_2 has the required value, the power delivered to the other resistor R_1 equals _____ watts.

P_m

Since R_1 is the internal resistance of the physical generator, the power delivered to it is dissipated and does nothing but heat up the generator. When R_2 is adjusted so that the maximum power is delivered to it, what fraction is this of the total power supplied by the voltage source? _____

One-half

6 EQUIVALENCE OF NETWORKS

The possibility of replacing one model of a source by an *equivalent* one was observed in Unit 3. The idea of what is meant by the equivalence of two networks will be further developed here.

In the diagrams below, two different networks are enclosed in dashed lines. A 2-ohm resistor is connected to the terminals of each one. The values of voltage and current for each network are given. Before you do anything else, verify that the values and relationships given are correct.

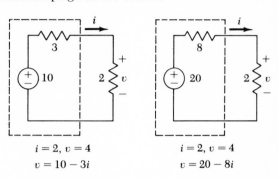

$$i = 2, v = 4$$
$$v = 10 - 3i$$

$$i = 2, v = 4$$
$$v = 20 - 8i$$

The values of v and i at the terminals of the two networks _____ (are/are not) the same.

are

The relationships between the voltage and current at the terminals of the two networks _____ (are/are not) the same.

are not

Two networks are defined to be equivalent at their terminals if (check one):

(a)

(a)   They have the same vi relationship at the terminals
(b)   They have the same voltage and current at the terminals

are not

The networks in the dashed boxes above _____ (are/are not) equivalent.

Write the vi relationships at the terminals of the following two networks and state whether or not they are equivalent.

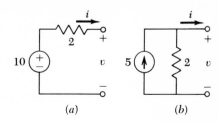

(a)   (b)

(a) $v = 10 - 2i$

(a) $v =$ _____ (in terms of i)

(b) $i = 5 - \dfrac{v}{2}$
or $v = 10 - 2i$

(b) $i =$ _____ (in terms of v)

Yes

$\dfrac{v}{2} = 5 - i$

is not

will

(a) $i = \dfrac{10}{2 + R}$

(b) $i = 5 - \dfrac{Ri}{2}$; solve for i

$i = \dfrac{5}{1 + R/2} = \dfrac{10}{2 + R}$

(b)

No

Are they equivalent? _____

In each network, let i_2 be the current in the resistor. In the left-hand network, i_2 is the same as i, the current at the terminals. Write an expression for i_2 (reference down) in terms of

i, in the right-hand network; $i_2 =$ _____. This current, i_2, _____ (is/is not) the same in the two networks.

Now let the first of these networks have a resistance R connected across its terminals. The network is then removed and replaced by the second one. No matter what the value of R might be, the current in R _____ (will/will not) be the same in the two cases. As an example, show this for the two networks above.

(a) $i =$ _____

(b) $i =$ _____

From the preceding, you can conclude that the property of equivalence of two networks applies to conditions (check one):

(a)   Internal to the terminals
(b)   External to the terminals
(c)   Both

7   TRANSFORMATION OF NETWORKS

The idea of equivalence can be used to advantage when solving a given network. At this point, you know procedures for finding the current in a series circuit or the voltage across one resistor in a series combination in terms of the voltage across the combination. Hence, if a given network can be transformed to a series circuit, through replacing part of a network by an equivalent, the solution can be completed.

Voltage v is to be found in the following network. Are all the components in series? _____

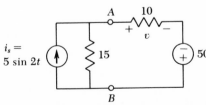

Suggest what to do to convert the network into a series connection of components, in which the 10-ohm resistor appears as one of the components.

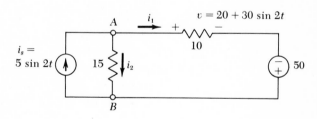

15   A

$75 \sin 2t$

B

_____

_____

Carry out this plan, and draw the new network. Now solve for v.

$v =$ _____

Once v is found in the transformed network, its value can be used in the original network to find other unknowns. The original diagram is redrawn below. With v as found above,

$v = 20 + 30 \sin 2t$

A i_1 + $-$
                  10
$i_s = 5 \sin 2t$ 15 i_2 50
B

i_1 becomes

$i_1 =$ _____

Then, from KCL applied to junction A,

$i_2 =$ _____

Why was it necessary to return to the original network to find

i_2? _____

Convert the following network into a series circuit and find the current i.

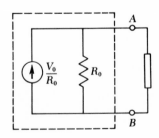

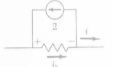

$i = \dfrac{5 - 10}{50} = -0.1$

$i = $ _____

up

The actual direction of i is _____ (down/up).

Now, in the original network, find the value of the voltage v_b across the current source.

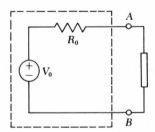

By KCL, $i_b = 2 - 0.1 = 1.9$

$v_b = 5i_b = 9.5$

or, by KVL

$v_b = 5 - (-0.1)(45)$

$v_b = $ _____

When a portion of a network (*a subnetwork*) is replaced by an equivalent, careful observance of the *meaning* of equivalence must be maintained. When we say that the networks in the two dashed rectangles below are equivalent, we mean that, so far as terminals AB are concerned, the relationship between

voltage and current is the same for the two. We say *nothing* about conditions within the dashed boxes (inside the two subnetworks).

Two diagrams for the first example are repeated below. The relationship between the subnetworks within the boxes is described by saying that they are _____. When the

equivalent

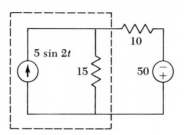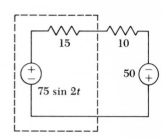

one on the left is replaced by the other, the current in the 10-ohm resistor _____ (will/will not) be the same. The current in the 15-ohm resistor _____ (will/will not) be the same; that is, when two networks each having two terminals are said to be equivalent, the property that this describes refers to conditions _____ (where?)

will

will not

external to the
terminals

8 PARALLEL CIRCUITS

In the preceding diagram, a method of procedure for finding the current in the 10-ohm resistor was to replace the box in the left-hand diagram with the one on the right. The result is a series circuit. Instead, suppose the other part of the network, namely, the 10-ohm resistor in series with the voltage source, is replaced by an appropriate equivalent. Draw a diagram of the resulting network and show the numerical values of the components. The components in this network _____ (are/are not) in series.

are not

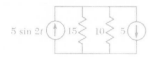

It can be seen that the voltages of the components are related to each other; they are all _____

equal, or the same

Branches of a network whose terminals are connected together in such a way that the branch voltages are the same are said to be *in parallel*. The result is also called a *parallel circuit*.

The term does not mean that the branches must be arranged in a geometrically parallel manner.

In the diagrams below, list those in which all branches are connected in parallel, are in series, or are neither.

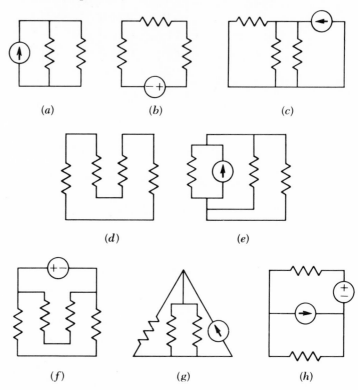

(a)   (b)   (c)

(d)   (e)

(f)   (g)   (h)

(a) Parallel: _____
(b) Series: _____
(c) Neither: _____

Just as two resistors *in series* can be replaced by an equivalent single resistor, so also a single resistor can replace two resistors *in parallel*. Two such resistors are shown below.

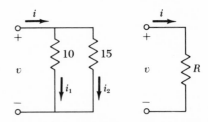

The single resistor R is to be equivalent to the parallel resistors. What does this mean in terms of v and i?

_____

_____

The vi relationships at the terminals must be the same.

For the single resistor, Ohm's law gives _____.
Apply Kirchhoff's law, and Ohm's law twice, to the parallel circuit and obtain the vi relationship.

$v = Ri$

$$i = i_1 + (\quad) = (\quad) v + (\quad) v = (\quad) v$$

$i_2; \dfrac{1}{10}; \dfrac{1}{15}; \dfrac{1}{6}$

Then state the required value of R.

$R = $ _____

6

It is useful to have a general formula for the equivalent of two resistors in parallel. In the above circuit, let the two resistors be labeled R_1 and R_2 (instead of the numerical values shown).

Repeat the above procedure for this general case

$i = \dfrac{v}{R_1} + \dfrac{v}{R_2}$

$i = $ _____ (in terms of v, R_1, and R_2)

$v = \dfrac{1}{1/R_1 + 1/R_2} i$

The equivalent resistance is

$R = \dfrac{R_1 R_2}{R_1 + R_2}$

$R = $ _____

In the case of parallel connections, it is convenient to think in terms of conductance, the reciprocal of resistance. From the previous result for R, write an expression for the equivalent conductance G in terms of the parallel conductances G_1 and G_2.

$G_1 + G_2$

(obtained from $G = \dfrac{1}{R}$

$= \dfrac{R_1 + R_2}{R_1 R_2} = G_1 + G_2$)

$G = $ _____

This form is simpler than the one for resistance.

A 50-ohm and a 100-ohm resistor are connected in parallel.

$\dfrac{1}{0.01 + 0.02} = 33.3$

The equivalent resistance equals _____ ohms.

smaller

This equivalent resistance is _____ (greater/smaller) than the resistance of each of the original resistors in the parallel connection.

The above conclusion regarding the magnitude of the equivalent resistance for a parallel connection is true for these two specific resistors. Now consider whether it is true for any two resistors. The conductance of the combination is $G = G_1 + G_2$

greater than

G is greater than G_2

and so G is _____ (greater than/less than) G_1. How are G and G_2 related? _____. With $G = 1/R$, $G_1 = 1/R_1$, and $G_2 = 1/R_2$, place corresponding inequality marks in the following:

$<$
$<$

$R \qquad R_1$

$R \qquad R_2$

When two resistors R_1 and R_2 are connected in parallel, the equivalent resistance is (check one):

(b)

(a) Always greater than one resistance and less than the other

(b) Always less than either of the two.

The diagram below shows four resistors in parallel. Let R be the equivalent resistance (and G the equivalent conductance). By applying KCL and Ohm's law,

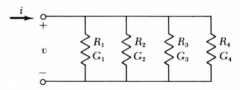

$G_1 + G_2 + G_3 + G_4$

$i = ($ _____ $)v$ in terms of G's

Write an expression for G in terms of the conductances G_1, G_2, etc, and for R in terms of R_1, R_2, etc.

(a) $G = G_1 + G_2 + G_3 + G_4$

(a) $G = $ _____

(b) $R = \dfrac{1}{\dfrac{1}{R_1} + \dfrac{1}{R_2} + \dfrac{1}{R_3} + \dfrac{1}{R_4}}$

(b) $R = $

The conclusion is that if two or more resistors are connected in parallel, they can be replaced by an equivalent resistor whose (check one):

(b)

(a) Resistance equals the sum of the individual resistances

(b) Conductance equals the sum of the individual conductances

The diagram below shows two current sources in parallel.

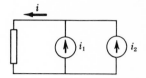

By KCL applied to the diagram, the current i of the combination is

$i_1 + i_2$

$i = \underline{\hspace{5cm}}$

If the reference for i_2 is reversed, the formula for i will become

$i_1 - i_2$

$i = \underline{\hspace{5cm}}$

If two or more current sources are connected in parallel, they can be replaced by an equivalent current source. If the reference of each current source is the same relative to their common junctions, the current of the equivalent source equals

the sum of the currents

$\underline{\hspace{6cm}}$

9   EXERCISES ON SERIES AND PARALLEL EQUIVALENT RESISTANCE

It is often desired to find the equivalent resistance at a pair of terminals of a network of resistors which are neither series nor parallel. Sometimes successive (one after the other) applications of the series and parallel rules can accomplish this.

Find the value of the resistance R equivalent to the following network. Draw a succession of diagrams showing the sequence of steps used. (Hint: First look for two different series combinations.)

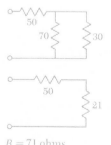

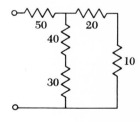

$R = 71$ ohms

$R = \underline{\hspace{5cm}}$

Find the value of the single resistance equivalent to each of the following networks. (Draw diagrams representing the steps used.)

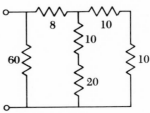

15 ohms

$R =$ _____

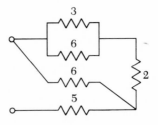

7.4 ohms

$R =$ _____

If you want more practice and want to see an interesting example, go on; otherwise proceed to Sec. 10.

A network having the structure shown below is called a *ladder* network. It is possible to find the equivalent resistance

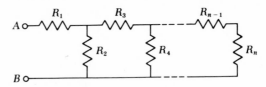

R at terminals AB by proceeding in the following way. We observe that R_1 is in series with the rest of the network, shown in the dashed box in the diagram below. Let the equivalent resistance of the dashed box be R_a; then $R = R_1 + R_a$. R_a in

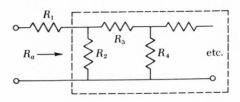

R_2

turn consists of R_2 in parallel with the remainder of the network. Let R_b be the resistance of this remainder. Thus, R_b is the resistance of that network to the right of _____ (which R?). We now have

$$R = R_1 + R_a \quad \text{and} \quad \frac{1}{R_a} = \frac{1}{R_2} + \frac{1}{R_b}$$

Thus,

$$R = R_1 + \cfrac{1}{\cfrac{1}{R_2} + \cfrac{1}{R_b}}$$

With R_b the pattern is repeated. That is,

$R_3 + \cfrac{1}{\cfrac{1}{R_4} + \cfrac{1}{R_d}}$

R_4

$$R_b = (\quad) + \cfrac{1}{\cfrac{1}{(\quad)} + \cfrac{1}{R_d}}$$

where R_d is the equivalent of everything to the right of _____ (which R?). Now substitute this in the above expression for R, and extend the process for the case $n = 6$ to give the following (R_6 is the last component).

$R_3 + \cfrac{1}{\cfrac{1}{R_4} + \cfrac{1}{R_5 + R_6}}$

$$R = R_1 + \cfrac{1}{\cfrac{1}{R_2} + \cfrac{1}{(\quad) + \cfrac{1}{(\quad) + (\quad)}}}$$

This mathematical form is called a *continued fraction*.

In the ladder network below, suppose nothing is connected to terminals CD. Find the equivalent resistance R at AB.

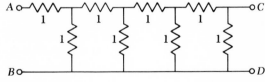

$\dfrac{34}{21}$

$R = $ _____

Now focus your attention on terminals CD, and assume that nothing is connected to AB. Find the equivalent resistance at CD. (Don't start from scratch, but use the preceding result.)

$\dfrac{13}{21}$

$R_{CD} = $ _____

10 FINDING VOLTAGES AND CURRENTS IN A PARALLEL CIRCUIT

For aesthetic reasons, the connections between the components in network diagrams are usually drawn as straight lines. Sometimes this tends to obscure the fact that a number of components are connected to a common junction.

In the following diagram, four specific places have been labeled with letters.

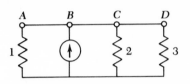

zero

Yes

Same

The voltage between A and B equals _____. There is no network component lying between A and B. In terms of electrical properties, would it be permissible to replace the top diagram by the one below? _____. Do points A and B represent separate junctions or the same one? _____

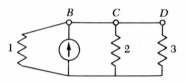

One

Yes

The same considerations also apply to the remaining points. What is the total number of junctions that the four points represent? _____

The arrangement in the first diagram above, in which there are a number of apparent junctions that really constitute a single junction, is called an *extended junction*. It arises only because we like to draw diagrams in orderly, straight-line configurations. Does Kirchhoff's current law apply to an extended junction? _____

Henceforth, whenever an extended junction occurs, it will be counted as a single junction.

The diagram on the following page shows some current sources and resistors connected in parallel.

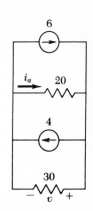

two

extended

2 amp

24

−1.2

One

There is a total of _____ junctions in this network. Each of these is an _____ junction. Construct an equivalent circuit consisting of a single current source and a single resistor, and label it appropriately. From this diagram find the value of voltage v.

$v = $ _____

Now find the current i_a in the 20-ohm resistor in the original network.

$i_a = $ _____

In the following diagram, how many junctions does the line from A to B represent? _____

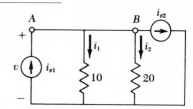

$i_{s1} - i_{s2}$

Taking a reference toward the upper junction, the net current from the current sources equals _____. Find expressions for the currents i_1 and i_2 in terms of i_{s1} and i_{s2} by any means you can.

$v = \dfrac{20}{3}(i_{s1} - i_{s2})$

(a) $i_1 = \dfrac{2}{3}(i_{s1} - i_{s2})$

(b) $i_2 = \dfrac{1}{3}(i_{s1} - i_{s2})$

(a) $i_1 = $ _____

(b) $i_2 = $ _____

This procedure is described as follows:

(a) Replace the two parallel current sources by an equivalent current source $i_{s1} - i_{s2}$.

(b) Replace the two parallel resistors by an equivalent resistor.

(c) Ohm's law

(c) Find the voltage across the branches by _____ (what law?).

(d) Return to the original diagram with the voltage now known and find each current by _____ (what law?).

(d) Ohm's law

11 CURRENT DIVIDER

In the preceding illustration, the current from the current sources is distributed, or *divided*, between the two parallel resistors in a particular ratio. Since this structure, namely, two parallel resistors fed by an equivalent current, occurs quite often, it would be useful to have a formula showing the way in which the current is distributed.

The diagram below shows the structure of two resistors in parallel fed by a current source. The voltage across each resistor _____ (is/is not) the same as the voltage v across the current source.

is

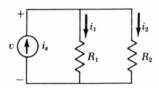

First the voltage v is determined, after the resistors are replaced by an equivalent, giving

$$v = i_s \left(\frac{R_1 R_2}{R_1 + R_2} \right)$$

Then Ohm's law gives each current. Thus, for i_2 we find

$$i_2 = \frac{1}{R_2} v = \frac{1}{R_2} i_s \frac{R_1 R_2}{R_1 + R_2}$$

or

$$i_2 = \frac{R_1}{R_1 + R_2} i_s$$

Use the same approach to find a similar expression for i_1.

$$\frac{R_2}{R_1 + R_2} i_s$$

$$i_1 = \underline{\hspace{5cm}}$$

Since the current is "divided" between the two resistors, the structure is called a *current divider*.

By comparing the expressions for the two currents in a current divider, we find that the larger resistor carries the

smaller

$$\underline{\hspace{3cm}} \text{(greater/smaller) current.}$$

Write the formulas

$$i_2 = \frac{R_1}{R_1 + R_2} i_s \qquad i_1 = \frac{R_2}{R_1 + R_2} i_s$$

completely in terms of $G_1 = 1/R_1$ and $G_2 = 1/R_2$. (*Hint:* Divide the numerator and denominator by $R_1 R_2$.)

(a) $\dfrac{G_1}{G_1 + G_2} i_s$

(a) $i_1 = \underline{\hspace{5cm}}$

(b) $\dfrac{G_2}{G_1 + G_2} i_s$

(b) $i_2 = \underline{\hspace{5cm}}$

The *current-divider formula* can be stated as follows:

The current in one resistor is to the total current as the conductance of that resistor is to the sum of the conductances.

Use this "verse" to write an expression for i_x in the diagram below (using G's).

$$\frac{i_x}{i} = \frac{G_x}{G_x + G_y}$$

$$i_x = \frac{G_x}{G_x + G_y} i$$

$$i_x = \underline{\hspace{5cm}}$$

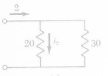

One possible answer:

$$i_2 = \frac{0.05}{0.05 + 0.0333} \, (2)$$

Another possible answer:

$$i_2 = \frac{30}{20 + 30} \, (2)$$
$$= 1.2$$

A 2-amp current flows into the parallel combination of two resistors having values of 20 and 30 ohms. Draw the diagram (showing all reference orientations), and find the value of the current i_2 in the 20-ohm resistor.

$i_2 = $ _____

12 AN ALTERNATE TRANSFORMATION

In an earlier example (repeated below), the part within the dashed rectangle was replaced by an equivalent to convert the result to a series circuit, since it was already known how to "solve" a series circuit.

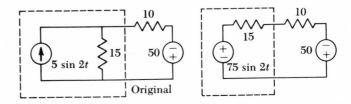

Original

As an alternate procedure replace the part of the original circuit outside the box by an equivalent circuit. Do it by completing the diagram below.

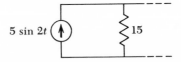

current divider

$$i_2 = (5 \sin 2t - 5) \left(\frac{0.0667}{0.1667}\right)$$
$$= 2 \sin 2t - 2$$

The result contains two current sources in parallel; they can be replaced by a single equivalent. After this is done, the structure of the result is that of a _____. Use the formula for this structure to find the current in the 15-ohm resistor. (Call it i_2 with reference downward.)

$i_2 = $ _____

Verify your answer by comparing it with the previously found value in Sec. 7.

Convert the following diagram to a parallel circuit and find the voltage v. Then use this in the original network to find i.

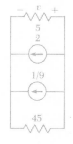

(a) $v = -9.5$

(b) $i = \dfrac{v+5}{45} = -0.1$

(a) $v =$ _____

(b) $i =$ _____

Two resistors R_1 and R_2 can be arranged as a current divider or as a voltage divider. Draw a diagram for each of these, and write an appropriate formula giving the current in R_1 in the current divider and the voltage across R_1 in the voltage divider.

Current divider

$i_1 = \dfrac{G_1}{G_1 + G_2} i$

Voltage divider

$v_1 = \dfrac{R_1}{R_1 + R_2} v$

13   SIMPLIFYING NETWORK STRUCTURES

"Solving" a circuit (finding values of voltage and current for each component) is simple when the circuit is a series combination or a parallel combination. The preceding sections dis-

cussed cases in which one or the other structure shown below
appeared as a subnetwork.

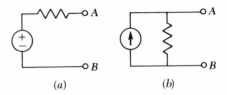

(a)   (b)

In some cases, when Fig. (b) was replaced by its equivalent,
Fig. (a) (with appropriate values), the result became a series
circuit. In other cases, when Fig. (a) was replaced by its
equivalent Fig. (b), the result became a parallel circuit. In
each of these cases, the solution could proceed to completion.
(For ease of reference, the one on the left will be called the
v-source equivalent and the one on the right the *i-source
equivalent*.)

In the network below, it is desired to find the voltage v_2
across R_2. For convenience in calculation, a set of numerical
values, shown alongside the resistors, will be used, but focus

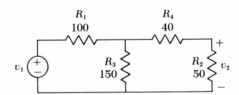

attention on the *process* being carried out, rather than on the
numerical values.

First replace the series combination of v_1 and R_1 by an *i*-
source equivalent. The result is shown below; it is neither a
series circuit nor a parallel circuit. Suggest a sequence of two

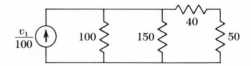

Combine R_1 in parallel with R_3 into an equivalent R. Replace this in parallel with the i source by a v-source equivalent.

voltage divider

$$\frac{50}{60 + 40 + 50} (0.6v_1) = 0.2v_1$$

steps that will convert this result into a series circuit. _____

_____

_____

_____

Carry out this sequence and draw the series circuit, showing all values.

For finding v_2, the structure can be considered a _____. Find v_2 in terms of v_1.

$v_2 =$ _____

The above example proceeded by a series of steps:

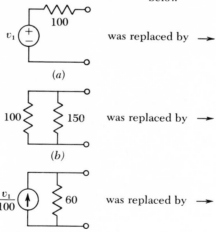

Draw the equivalents below

(a)   was replaced by →

(b)   was replaced by →

(c)   was replaced by →

The final result was a series circuit.

The following diagram is to be converted into a series circuit in which the current will be identical to current i. Show the sequence of steps in which a conversion to a v-source or i-source equivalent occurs, or resistors are combined. Show the result of each step opposite (a), (b), etc. Label each intermediate diagram with appropriate values.

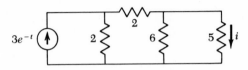

(a)   (b)

(a)   (b)

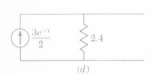

(c)   (d)

(c)

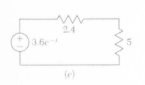

(e)

(d)

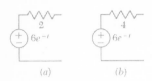

(e)

Now solve for i:

$$i = \frac{3.6e^{-t}}{2.4+5} = 0.485e^{-t}$$

$i = $ _____

14 THE THEVENIN EQUIVALENT

one

In each of the above examples, it was required to find the current or voltage in _____ (how many?) branch(es) of a network. The structure of the *rest* of the network was transformed, so that this branch appeared in series with two

a voltage source
and *one* resistor

things: _____(name them)

The diagrams of these examples are redrawn below. Each of the subnetworks within the dashed enclosure was replaced by an equivalent which has the same form for both. Draw this *form*.

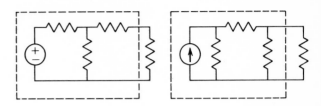

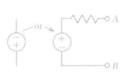

The above result is quite general and can be rigorously proved. It is important enough to be given a name; it is called the *Thevenin equivalent*; that is, given a network containing resistors and voltage and current sources, with two terminals exposed, as implied by the box shown below, the Thevenin equivalent consists of (in words): _____

a voltage source in
series with a resistor

_____

(Your statement should name the types of components and the manner of connection.) Draw the equivalent.

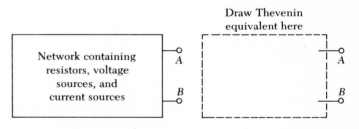

As you might suspect from the above, the source voltage and resistance in the above equivalent of a network having two terminals   are   called,   respectively,   the   _____
_____ voltage and the _____
resistance.

Thevenin equivalent
Thevenin equivalent

In the examples given, in order to find values of the Thevenin equivalent voltage and resistance, a process of successive transformations of networks to simple equivalent forms was used. For the network shown below, with respect to the terminals indicated, complete the Thevenin equivalent for each of the references shown to the right. Label each diagram with component values.

24

24

or resistors
can be here

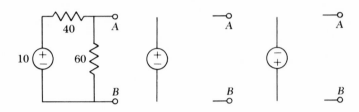

When replacing a given network by its Thevenin equivalent, it is essential, of course, to identify the *terminals* of the network and to place the Thevenin equivalent between the same terminals.

Thus, suppose that in the preceding diagram another pair of terminals are formed, as shown below. Draw a Thevenin equivalent at these terminals and find the values of the components.

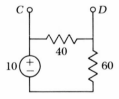

C   *D*

24

4

No   Is this equivalent identical with the previous one? _____

In the network below, it is desired to replace the current source in parallel with the 5-ohm resistor by a Thevenin equivalent.

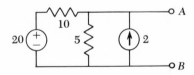

(a) The ends of the
     parallel combination
     are extended junctions;
     they can be redrawn as

Two possibilities are shown below, with the Thevenin equivalent placed in two different positions. Check the correct one.

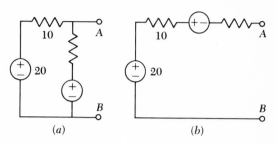

(a)   (b)

Yes

Referring to Figs. (b), (c), and (d) below, is each of them
electrically the same Thevenin equivalent as Fig. (a)?_____
(yes/no). If "no," list any that are different. _____

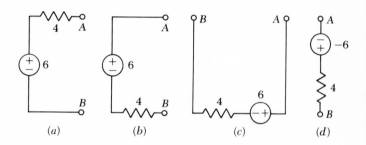

(a)   (b)   (c)   (d)

15   EXERCISES ON THE THEVENIN EQUIVALENT
When we say "find the Thevenin equivalent" of a given network at its terminals, we mean draw the equivalent and calculate the values of the components.

Find the Thevenin equivalent of the network below at terminals *AB*.

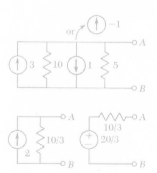

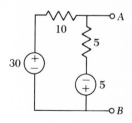

Find the Thevenin equivalent of the networks below, at the terminals labeled *AB*.

Find the Thevenin equivalent of the following network:

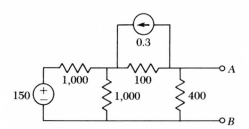

16 APPLICATION OF THEVENIN EQUIVALENT IN NETWORK SOLUTIONS

When it is desired to find the voltage or current in *one* branch of a network, replacing all but this branch by a _____ equivalent will lead to a _____ (series/parallel) circuit. From this, a solution for the desired voltage or current can be easily found. Once this voltage or current is known,

Thevenin

series

other branch voltages or currents can be determined from additional calculations in the *original* network. This is illustrated in the network on the preceding page. The Thevenin equivalent to the left of terminals AB was earlier (in Sec. 13) found to be the one shown on the right. From this, the voltage v_2 is found to be:

$0.2v_1$

$$v_2 = \rule{5cm}{0.4pt}$$

Now return to the original network. With v_2 known, the cur-

$\dfrac{v_2}{50} = \dfrac{0.2v_1}{50} = 0.004v_1$

rent i_2 in the 50-ohm resistor is $i_2 = \rule{3cm}{0.4pt}$. The

$40i_2 = 0.16v_1$

current in the 40-ohm resistor is the same, so that $v_4 = \rule{2cm}{0.4pt}$

Now the voltage across the 150-ohm resistor can be determined from KVL in terms of the known voltages v_2 and v_4. It

$v_4 + v_2 = 0.36v_1$

is $v_3 = \rule{3cm}{0.4pt}$. Finally, from KCL the current i_1

$\dfrac{v_3}{150} + i_2 = 0.0064v_1$

is found to be $i_1 = \rule{5cm}{0.4pt}$

Thus, once v_2 is known, all voltages and currents are found by a successive application of Ohm's law and |Kirchhoff's

original

laws to the $\rule{2.5cm}{0.4pt}$ (original/equivalent) network.

Earlier, for the network below, the equivalent on the right was found.

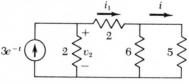
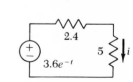

$0.486e^{-t}$

From this, the current i is found to be $i = \rule{3cm}{0.4pt}$.
Using the process just described, find i_1 and v_2:

(a) $i_1 = i + \dfrac{5i}{6}$

$\quad = \dfrac{11}{6} i = 0.891e^{-t}$

(a) $i_1 = \rule{6cm}{0.4pt}$

(b) $v_2 = 2\,(3e^{-t} - i_1)$
$\quad = 4.22e^{-t}$
(or $v_2 = 2i_1 + 5i = $ same)

(b) $v_2 = \rule{6cm}{0.4pt}$

The general method of solution discussed here involves (a) replacing a subnetwork by a Thevenin equivalent, (b) solving for a voltage or current for a single branch, and then (c) using this solution, together with known sources, in the *original network* to find other branch voltages or currents by suitable applications of Kirchhoff's laws and Ohm's law.

In the network below, find the voltage across each resistor. If you don't get the answers given, refer to the solution outlined below.

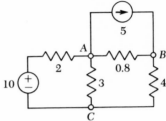

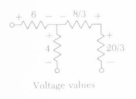

+ 6 − − 8/3 +

4   20/3

Voltage values

SOLUTION

As a first step, find two Thevenin equivalents, one for the portion on the left, including the 3-ohm resistor, and one for the current source in parallel with the 0.8-ohm resistor. From this, the voltage across the 4-ohm resistor is found (by use of the voltage-divider principle), and the current through it

1.2   0.8

6   4   4

$\frac{5}{3}$

$\frac{10}{3}$

$\frac{8}{3}$

(with reference downward) will equal _____. In the original diagram, from KCL applied to junction B, the current to the

left in the 0.8-ohm resistor will equal _____

The voltage across it will, therefore, equal _____

From the two voltages found so far, the voltage v_{AC} can be found by using KVL in the original diagram. The voltage across the 2-ohm resistor can then be found by KVL in the original diagram.

17   REMARK

One type of configuration that often occurs within a network is illustrated in the diagram below.

A

i ↓   5   +

C $v = 10$

6

−

B

The voltage across the series combination of a voltage source and resistor is known. It is desired to find the current in the resistor. By Ohm's law, the current is given by a voltage divided by the resistance. The correct voltage to use in the above is (check one):

(a)   The source voltage
(b)   The voltage across the resistor
(c)   The voltage v

In finding this voltage, which, in double subscript notation is v_{AC}, KVL is used, to yield

$$v_{AC} = v_{AB} + v_{BC} = 10 + (\qquad) = \text{_____}.$$

Thus, the current is:

$$i = \text{_____}$$

Use this approach to find the current in the 5-ohm resistor in the network below. Then find the open-circuit voltage at terminals AB.

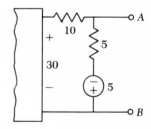

(b)

$(-6); 4$

$\dfrac{10 - 6}{5}$

$i_5 \text{ (down)} = \dfrac{30 + 5}{10 + 5} = \dfrac{7}{3}$

$v_{AB} = 5i_5 - 5 = \dfrac{20}{3}$

18   ALTERNATE EVALUATION OF THEVENIN EQUIVALENT VOLTAGE

The process by which the Thevenin equivalent has been found so far involves successive transformations of parts of the network until a simple form is obtained. You have seen specific examples without the emergence of a general principle. The exposition of the general principle is the next step.

An arbitrary network containing resistors and voltage and current sources is symbolized by the box on the left below; on the right is its Thevenin equivalent.

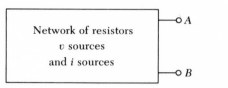 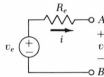

(a) Thevenin equivalent resistance

(a) R_e is called the _____

(b) Thevenin equivalent voltage

(b) v_e is called the _____

They are the same.

When we say these two networks are equivalent at terminals AB, what do we mean about their vi relationship? _____. Suppose an arbitrary resistance R is connected to terminals AB. Will the voltage across this resistance be the same for both networks? _____. Write the vi relationship for the Thevenin equivalent network.

Yes

$v_e - R_e i$

$v =$ _____

Suppose the terminals are left open. What will be the value of the terminal voltage v of the Thevenin equivalent in this case? $v =$ _____. Will the terminal voltage *of the original network* also be equal to this when the terminals are left open? _____

$v = v_e$

Yes

As a result of the preceding, describe a procedure for finding the Thevenin equivalent voltage v_e of a given network.

Leave the terminals open and find the *open-circuit* terminal voltage.

Find v_e for the portion to the left of AB in the circuit below.

No current in the 80-ohm resistor; ∴

$$v_{AB} = \frac{70}{30+70} \times 10 = 7 = v_e$$

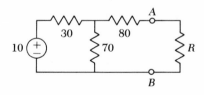

For the diagram below, find the Thevenin equivalent voltage for the network with respect to terminals AB.

Method 1 (current divider).
In 10-ohm resistor:

$$i = 5\left(\frac{1/16}{1/4 + 1/16}\right)$$

$$= \frac{5}{4+1} = 1 \text{ (down)}$$

$$v_e = 10i = 10 \text{ volts}$$

Method 2. Convert to:

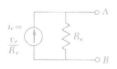

$$v_e = 20\left(\frac{10}{4+6+10}\right) = 10$$

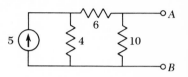

The general method of finding R_e is given in Sec. 20.

19   NORTON EQUIVALENT

The Thevenin equivalent of a given network at a pair of terminals is a voltage source v_e in series with a resistor R_e, as shown below. But you already know another network which is equivalent to this one with respect to terminals AB. Draw this network and express the values of its components in terms of those of the Thevenin equivalent.

is

is

This equivalent is called a *Norton equivalent*. It _____ (is/is not) possible to find the component values of the Norton equivalent from those of the Thevenin equivalent. The Norton equivalent _____ (is/is not) the current source equivalent of the Thevenin equivalent.

The Thevenin equivalent of a certain network is found to be the one shown below. Find and draw the Norton equivalent, including component values.

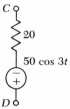

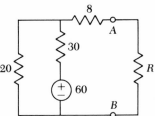

2.5 cos 3t   20

Thevenin equivalent is:

20

24

1.2   20

Find and draw the Norton equivalent of the portion of the following network to the left of AB, by first obtaining the Thevenin equivalent.

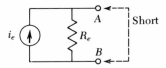

Norton
(Not i source, because it is said to be equivalent to a network, not a source)

The structure shown below is the _____ equivalent of a network. Suppose the terminals are connected together

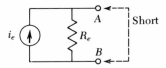

i_e

is

is not

Short-circuit the terminals and find the current in the short.

(short-circuited). The value of the current in the short circuit will be $i_{AB} =$ _____. If the terminals of the original network (not the Norton equivalent) are short-circuited, then the value of the current in this short circuit _____ (is/is not) the same as i_e. To find the Norton equivalent current i_e of a given network it _____ (is/is not) first required to find the Thevenin equivalent. How can it be obtained from the original diagram? _____

It is desired to find the Norton equivalent current for the network to the right of AB in the diagram shown below. (*Hint:* Does the 80-ohm resistor affect the short-circuit current?)

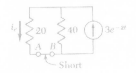

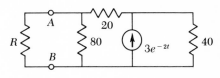

Current divider:

$$i_e = \frac{1/20}{1/20 + 1/40} \, 3e^{-2t} = 2e^{-2t}$$ $i_e =$ _____

Find the Norton equivalent current for the network to the left of the terminals AB in the diagram below.

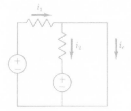

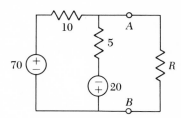

Use KCL:

$$i_e = i_1 - i_2$$

By KVL:

$$70 - 10i_1 = 0 \,, \therefore\, i_1 = 7$$
$$20 - 5i_2 = 0 \,, \therefore\, i_2 = 4$$

$$i_e = 3$$

$i_e =$ _____

20 THEVENIN (OR NORTON) EQUIVALENT RESISTANCE

The Thevenin equivalent voltage v_e of a network at a pair of terminals equals _____

the open-circuit voltage

The Norton equivalent current i_e of a network at a pair of terminals equals _____

the short-circuit current

Each of the two quantities v_e and i_e can be found as specified above. Describe a simple way to find the equivalent resistance R_e in terms of v_e and i_e. _____

Take ratio $\frac{v_e}{i_e}$

There is another way to obtain R_e, as we shall now show. Imagine a network containing resistors and sources, with terminals AB at which the Thevenin equivalent is required, and imagine the Thevenin equivalent with source voltage v_e and resistance R_e. Then assume that the voltages of all voltage sources and the currents of all current sources in the given network are reduced to zero. Now observe the following facts pertinent to that condition: (a) the open-circuit voltage v_{AB} of the given network will then equal zero; (b) the given network and the Thevenin equivalent must still be equivalent; (c) therefore, the source voltage v_e of the Thevenin equivalent will equal

zero

R_e

zero

_____. It is concluded that the Thevenin equivalent now consists of a single resistor labeled _____; and that its resistance is equivalent to the resistance of the original network when all sources are set equal to _____

In connection with the process of reducing all sources to zero, it is noted that a voltage source is set equal to zero by

short

open

replacing it by a(n) _____ (short/open) circuit, and a current source is set equal to zero by replacing it by a(n) _____ (short/open) circuit. When this is done, the original network will contain resistors only. Then, the Thevenin equivalent resistance R_e can be found by using any appropriate method of reducing a network of resistors to an equivalent resistance.

The Norton equivalent current of the following network was found in Sec. 19 to be $i_e = 3$. Find R_e using both methods described above.

$$v_e = \frac{(70 + 20)\,5}{15} - 20$$

$$= 10$$

$$R_e = \frac{v_e}{i_e} = \frac{10}{3}$$

With sources removed:

$$R_e = \frac{5\,(10)}{5 + 10} = \frac{10}{3}$$

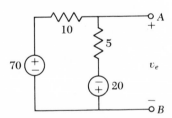

The Norton equivalent of the network on the next page was found in Sec. 19 by first finding the Thevenin equivalent. Now find the Norton equivalent by using the open-circuit voltage and short-circuit current. Compute R_e by both methods.

$$v_\nu = \frac{20}{50}(60) = 24$$

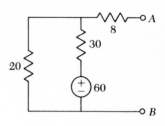

Method 1 (for i_c):

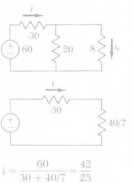

$$i_c = \frac{0.125\,(2)}{0.125 + 0.033 + 0.05} = 1.2$$

Method 2 (for i_c):

$$i = \frac{60}{30 + 40/7} = \frac{42}{25}$$

From top diagram: .

$$i_c = \frac{0.125}{0.175}\, i = 1.2$$

$$R_c = \frac{v_c}{i_c} = \frac{24}{1.2} = 20$$

With sources removed:

$$R_c = 8 + \frac{20\,(30)}{20 + 30}$$
$$= 20$$

21   APPLICATIONS IN DESIGN

The preceding parts of this unit have discussed procedures for "solving a network," that is, computing voltages and currents of all branches when component values and sources are given. Often, instead, it may be required to find the value of one or more components in order that the voltage or current of some branch, or the power to be dissipated in some branch, shall have a prespecified value.

To solve such problems, no new principles are needed. The same basic equations and procedures apply, but now the unknown is not a voltage or current but a component value.

As an illustration, consider the following diagram which shows a Wheatstone bridge. It is desired to find the value of

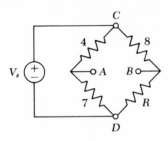

R for which $v_{AB} = 0$. The problem can be solved by finding an expression for v_{AB} in terms of the network components; then setting it to zero and solving for R.

Carry out the solution and verify your answer at the arrow below. If you need assistance, follow the solution given below, but only to the extent necessary.

SOLUTION

Is there anything directly connected between A and B? _____. Focus on the 4- and 7-ohm resistors. How are they connected? _____. The voltage across this combination equals _____. By the voltage-divider formula, $v_{AD} = $ _____

By similar reasoning, $v_{BD} = $ _____ volts.

By KVL around loop ADB, and using the preceding equations, v_{AB} in terms of R becomes $v_{AB} = $ _____

Since v_{AB} is to equal 0, _____

$R = $ _____

Another design problem is illustrated in the diagram below. The two unknown resistors have the same value R. It is desired to find the value of R for which the voltage v_2 has its maximum possible value. Find R.

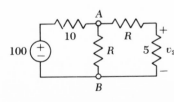

Margin notes:

No

In series

V_s

$\dfrac{7}{4+7}V_s = \dfrac{7}{11}V_s$

$\dfrac{R}{R+8}V_s$

$v_{AD} - v_{BD}$

$= \left(\dfrac{7}{11} - \dfrac{R}{R+8}\right)V_s$

14 ohms   ⟵

SOLUTION

If v_2 is to be maximized, the first task would seem to be to find an expression for v_2 in terms of R. The diagram can be reduced to a series circuit which includes the 5-ohm resistor. Do it.

The expression for v_2 will be (after algebraic simplification)

$$v_2 = \underline{\hspace{6cm}}$$

The maximum value of v_2 can be found mathematically by \underline{\hspace{3cm}}. Do it and find the required value of R.

$R =$ \underline{\hspace{3cm}} ohms

In each of the above design problems, the value of a single unknown resistance has to be found in order to satisfy a single condition. In other problems, it may be desired to satisfy more than one condition. In such cases, it will be possible to determine more than one resistance value. An illustration is given in the following problem.

A physical generator is to supply current to a load R_L. However, it is desired to reduce the level of the current by a large factor by inserting an *attenuator* (network of resistors) between the source and load (as shown below) without disturbing the generator; that is, the current supplied at the terminals of the generator is to be the same whether the attenuator is inserted or the load is connected directly to the generator. In this case

$$\frac{500R}{R^2 + 25R + 50}$$

differentiating

$\sqrt{50}$

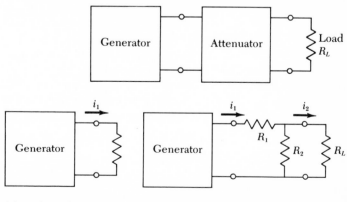

(*a*) Without Attenuator   (*b*) With Attenuator

suppose the attenuator consists of two unknown resistors as shown at (b) on the previous page.

Let $R_L = 1,000$ ohms and the current attenuation factor be 0.1; that is, $i_2 = i_1/10$. Design the attenuator; that is, determine the required values of R_1 and R_2 to achieve this level of attenuation, while maintaining i_1 the same in Figs. (a) and (b).

SOLUTION

If i_1 is to have the same values in Figs. (a) and (b), what value should the equivalent resistance connected to the generator terminals have in Fig. (b)? _____. Write an expression for this resistance in terms of R_1, R_2, and R_L.

$R_L = 1,000$

$$R_L = R_1 + \frac{R_L R_2}{R_L + R_2}$$

parallel

R_2 and R_L are connected in _____. The current in one branch of such a structure (which is i_2) can be written in terms of the total current into the combination (which is _____) by the _____

i_1; current-divider

formula. The result is

$$\frac{R_2}{R_2 + R_L} i_1$$

$$i_2 = \underline{\hspace{6cm}}$$

The solutions of the preceding two equations for R_1 and R_2 are:

(a)   900

(a) $R_1 = \underline{\hspace{3cm}}$ ohms

$\longleftarrow$

(b) $\dfrac{1,000}{9}$

(b) $R_2 = \underline{\hspace{3cm}}$ ohms

The same approach can be used to obtain general design formulas to be used with any load resistance and any attenuating factor. Instead of 0.1, let the attenuating factor be $1/a$; and let the load resistance be R_L rather than 1,000. Obtain formulas for R_1 and R_2 in terms of a and R_L.

(a) $R_2 = \dfrac{R_L}{a - 1}$

(a) $R_2 = \underline{\hspace{5cm}}$

(b) $R_1 = \left(\dfrac{a - 1}{a}\right) R_L$

(b) $R_1 = \underline{\hspace{5cm}}$

22 REQUIRED SOURCE VOLTAGE FOR SPECIFIED LOAD

Another type of problem is one in which the desired voltage, current, or power in one or more branches is specified and the required source voltage is desired. Again, no new principles are needed to solve such problems. Successive applications of Kirchhoff's two laws, the use of a Thevenin and Norton equivalent, and other procedures are applicable.

To illustrate, consider the following network. The resistor

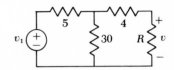

R represents a load across which the voltage v is specified to be a constant 100 volts. The power to be dissipated in R is also specified; it is $p = 500$ watts. The problem is to find the source voltage v_1.

A number of approaches are possible. Knowing both the power and voltage, the current in R will be $i_R =$ _____.

$$\frac{500}{100} = 5$$

From this, the voltage across the 4-ohm resistor will equal _____. By KVL, the voltage across the 30-ohm resistor can be found, and from this the current in it is found to equal _____, with reference _____ (up/down). The current in the 5-ohm resistor can now be found from KCL; it equals _____, with reference _____ (right/left). After finding the voltage across the 5-ohm resistor, finally $v_1 =$ _____ volts.

$$4(5) = 20$$

$$4;\ \text{down}$$

$$9;\ \text{right}$$

$$9(5) + 20 + 100 = 165$$

In the preceding process, starting at one end of the network, successive applications of Kirchhoff's laws and Ohm's law lead to a determination of all branch variables, finally arriving at a determination of the desired unknown. This procedure does not explicitly use the value of R in the calculations. Alternate procedures that do explicitly use the value of R are also possible.

As an example, from the originally given data, find R.

$$\frac{v^2}{p} = \frac{10,000}{500} = 20 \text{ ohms}$$

$$R = \text{_____}$$

Method 1:
Replace the network to the left of R by the Thevenin equivalent

$$6\frac{v_1}{7} \;\substack{\circlearrowleft \\ +\\ -} \qquad 4 + \frac{30}{7}$$

$$100 = \left(\frac{20}{20 + 4 + 30/7}\right)\left(\frac{6v_1}{7}\right)$$

$$v_1 = 165 \text{ volts}$$

Method 2:
Let i be current up in source; use current divider and Ohm's law:

$$100 = R\left(\frac{30}{30 + 24}\right) i$$

$$i = 9$$

To relate i to v_1, replace by an equivalent resistance

$$\substack{4} \qquad 30 \qquad R = 20$$

$$\substack{i} \qquad 5 \qquad v_1 \qquad 40/3$$

$$v_1 = \left(5 + \frac{40}{3}\right) i = 165$$

With R known, a number of different approaches can be taken to solve the problem. Use any approach you can to get a solution.

As another illustration, consider the following diagram which represents a three-wire dc power distribution system. The

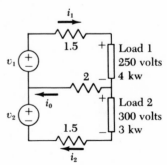

resistors shown represent the line resistances of the connecting wires. The power and voltage required by each load are specified, and it is desired to determine the required values of generator voltage v_1 and v_2.

By KVL, $v_1 = 1.5i_1 + 250 + 2i_0$. Hence, to complete the determination of v_1, it is necessary to know the line currents i_1 and i_0. From the data given on load 1, the value of i_1 is

$\dfrac{4{,}000}{250} = 16$ amp

_____. Similarly, from the data on load 2, the value

$\dfrac{3{,}000}{300} = 10$ amp

of i_2 is _____

$i_1 - i_2 = 6$ amp; 286 volts

Then, by KCL, $i_0 =$ _____. So, $v_1 =$ _____

By a similar approach, find v_2.

303 volts

$v_2 =$ _____

23 REVIEW PROBLEMS

Solve each of the following problems and verify your answers at the arrows shown at the end of the solutions. If you need assistance, follow the solution outlined below, but only to the extent needed.

PROBLEM 1

A certain 0.4-watt lamp bulb is designed to operate with 2 volts across its terminals. The only source available is a 3-volt battery with an internal resistance of $\frac{1}{3}$ ohm. A resistance R is placed in parallel with the bulb and the combination is placed in series with the battery and a 3-ohm resistor. Find the value of R needed for the bulb to operate at design voltage.

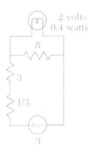

SOLUTION

The first thing to do in any problem is to draw the diagram. With 2 volts across the bulb and 0.4 watts of power, the bulb

$$\frac{0.4}{2} = 0.2$$

current = _____ amp. The voltage across the

$$\frac{3-2}{3+0.33} = \frac{3}{10}$$

(3 + 1/3)-ohm resistors can be found and so the current in these resistors equals _____. By KCL, this current in

$$0.2 + \frac{2}{R}$$

terms of other currents will be 3/10 = _____

20 ohms   ←   R = _____ (include unit of measure)

PROBLEM 2
Find i_1 and i_2 in the following network.

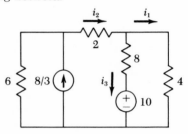

ONE POSSIBLE SOLUTION
To find i_1, the network to the left of the 4-ohm resistor can be replaced by a Thevenin equivalent. Find it.

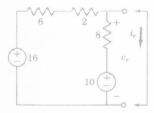

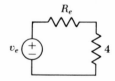

$$v_e = 8\left(\frac{16-10}{6+2+8}\right) + 10 = 13 \qquad v_e = \underline{\hspace{5cm}}$$

$$i_v = \frac{16}{6+2} + \frac{10}{8} = \frac{13}{4} \qquad\qquad i_e = \underline{\hspace{5cm}}$$

$$R_e = \frac{v_e}{i_e} = 4 \qquad\qquad\qquad R_e = \underline{\hspace{5cm}}$$

Also, with sources removed:
$R_v = 8$ ohms in parallel
with $6 + 2$ ohms.

$$i_1 = \frac{13}{4+4} = \frac{13}{8} \qquad\qquad ← \qquad i_1 = \underline{\hspace{5cm}}$$

$$4i_1 = \frac{13}{2}$$

To find i_2, return to the original network, with i_1 now known. The voltage across the 4-ohm resistor equals _____.

$$\frac{13}{2} - 10 = -\frac{7}{2}$$

By KVL, around the right-hand loop, the voltage across the 8-ohm resistor with reference + at top equals _____

By KCL:

$$i_2 = i_1 + i_3$$

$$= \frac{13}{8} - \frac{7}{16} = \frac{19}{16}$$

$\longleftarrow$ $i_2 =$ _____

PROBLEM 3

It is desired to determine the Thevenin equivalent of a laboratory power supply by making two voltage measurements, with two different resistors connected at the terminals. When a 10-ohm resistor is connected to the supply terminals, the measured voltage is 10.42 volts. When a 2-ohm resistor is connected to the terminals, the measured voltage is 6.85 volts. Find v_e and R_e.

SOLUTION

Draw a diagram of the arrangement. Express the measured load voltage for each resistor in terms of v_e by means of the voltage-divider formula. This will result in two equations for the two unknowns v_e and R_e.

$$10.42 = \frac{10 v_e}{10 + R_e}$$

$$6.85 = \frac{2 v_e}{2 + R_e}$$

12 volts

1.5 ohms

$\longleftarrow$ $v_e =$ _____

        $R_e =$ _____

PROBLEM 4

Knowing that you are studying engineering, the foreman of a small shop that uses electric ovens for baking enamel has asked you for help. He is blowing fuses and cannot figure what peak currents he should expect. He gives you a block diagram of his system as shown below. After some measurements, you are able to make a reasonable model, as shown underneath. He has been using fuses with the following capacities: F_1 and F_3, 50 and F_2, 15 amp. The problem is to determine fuse sizes that will permit an approximately 50 percent overload before blowing; that is, they will permit 50 percent more current than expected in the model. Assume fuse sizes are in multiples of 5. Determine what fuse sizes he should use.

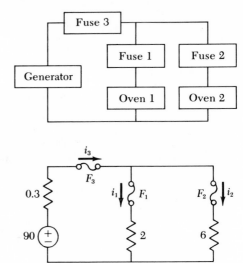

Fuse resistances are negligible

SOLUTION

Suppose i_3 were known. Write an expression for i_1 in terms of i_3.

By current divider:

$$i_1 = \frac{6}{2+6}\, i_3 = \frac{3}{4}\, i_3$$

$i_1 =$ _____

Similarly, write an expression for i_2 in terms of i_3.

$$i_2 = \frac{2}{8}\, i_3 = \frac{1}{4}\, i_3$$

$i_2 =$ _____

Now find i_3:

$$i_3 = \frac{90}{0.3 + 2(6)/(2+6)}$$

$$= \frac{90}{1.8} = 50 \text{ amp}$$

$i_3 =$ _____

The fuse sizes should be

F_1: 60

F_2: 20 ⟵

F_3: 75

F_1: _____

F_2: _____

F_3: _____

PROBLEM 5

In the diagram below, the unknown resistor R dissipates 12 watts power. Find the value of R.

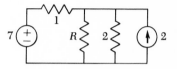

$$c + \frac{v}{R} + \frac{v}{2} = 9$$

$$v = \frac{9}{3/2 + 1/R}$$

$$\frac{v^2}{R}$$

$$\frac{1}{R}\left(\frac{9}{3/2 + 1/R}\right)^2 = 12$$

$$\frac{1}{3} \text{ or } \frac{4}{3} \quad ⟵$$

SOLUTION

Convert into a parallel circuit including R as one of the parallel components. Let v be the voltage across R. Write an expression for v in terms of R.

In terms of v the power dissipated in R is $p =$ _____.

Since p is known, the expression for v can be inserted here.

Then

$R =$ _____ ohms.

PROBLEM 6

In the diagram below, the voltage source delivers twice as much power as the current source. Find the value of R for which this condition is satisfied.

p supplied by i source
$\quad = 2(10) = 20$ watts

p supplied by v source
$\quad = 2(20) = 40$ watts

p dissipated in R
$$\quad = \frac{10^2}{R} = 20 + 40$$

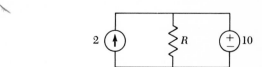

$R = \frac{5}{3} \quad ⟵$

$R =$ _____

PROBLEM 7

In the network below, determine the value of R which will make the voltage v a maximum.

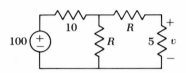

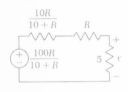

$$v = \frac{5}{R + 5 + 10R/(R + 10)}$$

$$\times \left(\frac{100R}{R + 10} \right) = \frac{500R}{R^2 + 25R + 50}$$

$$\frac{dv}{dR} = 500 \, (R^2 + 25R + 50$$

$$\frac{-2R^2 - 25R)}{(\text{denom})^2}$$

Setting $\frac{dv}{dR} = 0$, gives

$$R = \sqrt{50} \qquad \longleftarrow$$

SOLUTION

Replace a subnetwork by a Thevenin equivalent to get a series circuit including the 5-ohm resistor.

Once an expression for v is available in terms of R, employ the usual process to find a maximum?

$R = $ _____

PROBLEM 8

In the diagram below, find the value of R so that the power dissipated in R is a maximum, and find the value of this maximum power

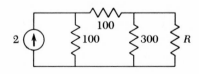

SOLUTION

If the subnetwork to the left of R is replaced by its Thevenin equivalent, then maximum power will occur when $R = R_e$.

$v_e = \dfrac{3}{5}(200) = 120$

$i_e = \dfrac{1}{2}(2) = 1$

$R = R_e = 120$ ohms

$R =$ _____

$P_m = \dfrac{v_R^{\,2}}{R} = \dfrac{(v_e/2)^2}{R_e}$

$\quad = 30$ watts

$P_m =$ _____

PROBLEM 9

Two dc generators are connected in parallel to supply power to a small manufacturing plant. The open-circuit voltages of the generators are v_1 and v_2, and the internal resistances are R_1 and R_2, respectively. The resistance of the lines from the power house to the plant can be neglected. In the plant, an 18-ohm oven is connected to the line as a load. Also, $R_1 = 3$ ohms and $R_2 = 6$ ohms.

Find expressions for the voltage v across the load and the currents i_1 and i_2, respectively, in each generator in terms of v_1 and v_2. Also find the power delivered to the load in terms of v_1 and v_2.

SOLUTION

A diagram is shown below. A Thevenin equivalent of the gen-

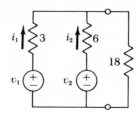
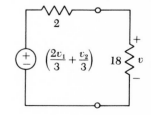

erators is also shown. By the voltage-divider formula, $v = 18v_e/20$. So,

$v = 0.6v_1 + 0.3v_2$

$v =$ _____

The current i_1 equals the voltage *across* R_1 (with load references) divided by 3. The same applies for i_2. So,

(a) $i_1 = \dfrac{v_1 - v}{3}$

$= \dfrac{0.4v_1 - 0.3v_2}{3}$ ⟵

(a) $i_1 = $ _____

(b) $i_2 = \dfrac{v_2 - v}{6}$

$= \dfrac{0.7v_2 - 0.6v_1}{6}$ ⟵

(b) $i_2 = $ _____

The load power is $p = v^2/18$. So, in terms of v_1 and v_2,

$0.02\,(v_1{}^2 + v_1\,v_2 + 0.25v_2{}^2)$

$p = $ _____

PROBLEM 10
The diagram below depicts an attenuator inserted between a source and a load R_L. Whether the load is connected directly to the source or the attenuator is inserted between the two should not change the voltage at the generator. The factor by which the voltage is to be attenuated is $1/a$; that is, $v_2/v_1 = 1/a$. Design the attenuator; that is, determine R_1 and R_2 in terms of a and R_L.

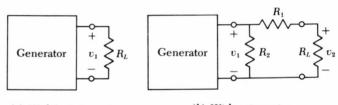

(*a*) Without attenuator   (*b*) With attenuator

SOLUTION
The equivalent resistance at the terminals of the generator in Fig. (*b*) is R_L. So,

$$R_L = \frac{R_2\,(R_1 + R_L)}{R_1 + R_2 + R_L}$$

In Fig. (*b*) the voltage ratio is not affected by R_2. From the voltage divider,

$$\frac{v_2}{v_1} = \frac{R_L}{R_1 + R_L} = \frac{1}{a}$$

The solution of these two equations gives the answer.

$R_1 = (a - 1) R_L$ $\longleftarrow$ $R_1 =$ _____

$R_2 = \dfrac{a}{a - 1} R_L$ $\longleftarrow$ $R_2 =$ _____

24 INTRODUCTION TO GENERAL METHODS OF ANALYSIS (REFERENCE SECTION)

In the preceding sections, the procedures used to "solve a network" involve replacing a subnetwork by an equivalent, thus reducing the structure to a simple one (series or parallel) for which a single equation with only one unknown can be written. After this, other branch currents or voltages can be found in a sequence of steps applied to the original network.

These procedures can be carried out in many cases, as verified by previous examples, but there are some cases for which they will not work (for example, certain problems involving bridge circuits). An alternative that will always succeed will now be presented.

The alternative approach is to apply the basic laws (Kirchhoff's two laws and Ohm's law) to the junctions and closed loops of the network to arrive at a set of *simultaneous equations* in a number of unknowns. Solving these equations simultaneously produces solutions for all the unknowns. A number of different sets of equations are possible, by employing different sets of variables. The process of arriving at these equations is simplified if, at the outset, we agree to choose references so that, for each resistor in a network, the voltage and current references form a *load set*. This permits $v = +Ri$ (or $i = +Gv$) to be written for each resistor.

In the example shown below, the voltage and current references for each resistor are chosen in accordance with the above stipulation. In this example, there are eight unknowns:

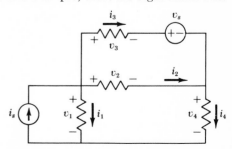

four voltages and four currents. A set of eight independent simultaneous equations would, therefore, be expected to yield all solutions. However, some of these equations will be of the simple form

$$v_1 = R_1 i_1 \quad \text{or} \quad i_1 = G_1 v_1$$
$$v_2 = R_2 i_2 \quad \text{or} \quad i_2 = G_2 v_2$$
$$\text{etc.}$$

which permits substitution of v_1 for i_1 (or vice versa), etc., in other equations, thereby cutting the number of unknowns in half. We shall also find other simple relationships among the variables, which reduce still further the number of equations to be solved simultaneously.

The topics that we shall investigate for a given network are:

(a)   What variables to choose
(b)   How many simultaneous equations will be required
(c)   How to write the equations

There are several ways to write a set of equations that will yield a complete solution for a network. Of these, we shall consider only two:

(a)   The method of node voltages
(b)   The method of mesh currents

In the *final* formulation of these two methods of analysis, it is not necessary to show references for each resistor current or voltage. Furthermore, it is sometimes more convenient to use G rather than R; hence, there is no preference in labeling each resistor with a G label or an R label. Accordingly, we shall frequently label diagrams in the manner shown below, with branch numbers in parentheses. These are not resistance or conductance values. The symbol for the resistance of the branch labeled (1) will be R_1, and its conductance will be G_1, etc.

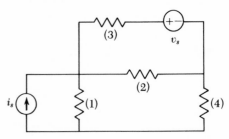

25   THE METHOD OF NODE VOLTAGES

Consider the following network, which contains four resistors and a known current source. The current and the voltage of

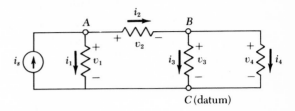

$$C\,(\text{datum})$$

each resistor are unknown. Let one of the junctions, say junction C, be selected as a *datum junction* (sometimes called a *ground*) and let us write KCL equations at the other two junctions, taking "away" as the junction reference. The result will be

A: $-i_s + i_1 + i_2 = 0$
B: $-i_2 + i_3 + i_4 = 0$

four

In these two equations there is a total of _____ unknowns. Add these two equations and write the result.

$-i_s + i_1 + i_3 + i_4 = 0$

datum

There is another junction in the above diagram called the _____ junction. Write the KCL equation at this junction, again taking "away" as the junction reference, and compare it with the preceding one.

(Same equation but multiplied by -1)

Yes

Can the KCL equation at junction C be obtained from those at junctions A and B? _____. Is the KCL equation at junction C independent of those at the other two junctions?

No

This is an example of a result that can be proved in general for all networks; namely, that the KCL equation at any one junction can be obtained by taking the negative sum of the KCL equations at all the other junctions—assuming all junction references are the same. We shall not prove it here but, in a network with N_j junctions, only N_j–1 independent KCL equations can be written.

Suppose a network has five junctions. If KCL equations are written at all the junctions, they _____ (will/will not) all be independent. How many KCL equations will be independent? _____

will not

Four

Return now to the original network (repeated below) and the KCL equations at junctions A and B.

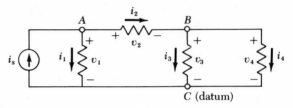

$$i_1 + i_2 = i_s$$
$$-i_2 + i_3 + i_4 = 0$$

(The known source current has been transposed to the right.) The unknowns here are all currents. The original network is labeled so that the current and voltage for each resistor form a _____ set of references.

load

Use Ohm's law to rewrite the above equations in terms of the resistor voltages; for convenience, use symbols for conductance rather than for resistance.

$G_2 v_2 = i_s$

$-G_2 v_2 + G_3 v_3 + G_4 v_4 = 0$

$G_1 v_1 + $ _____

_____

The total number of unknowns in these two equations is _____

four

In arriving at the last two equations, KCL and Ohm's law have been used. Which one of the three basic laws has not been used? _____. This law provides relationships among branch voltages. Each relationship can be used to express one voltage in terms of others. Hence, we can expect to reduce the number of unknowns in the last pair of equations by the number of *independent* KVL equations. However, all possible KVL equations that can be written are not independent. A specific procedure can be established which automatically takes care of this problem by providing only independent relationships. For this purpose, we define a set of node voltages. *The node voltage for a given junction is the voltage from that junction to the datum junction.* Using the definition just given, how many node voltages are there in the above network? _____

KVL

Two

v_B

A

B

datum

five

The node voltage from junction A to the datum is labeled v_A; the node voltage from junction B to the datum would be labeled _____. The reference plus sign for v_A is at which junction, A or the datum? _____. For v_B, which junction? _____

Although a set of node voltages was defined with a specific network as an illustration, this is a general procedure for any network. One junction of a network is selected as a _____ junction. If there is a total of six junctions in the network, the number of node voltages will be _____

26 RESISTOR VOLTAGES IN TERMS OF NODE VOLTAGES

Looking at the original network, each resistor voltage can be expressed in terms of one or more node voltages. For some cases, a resistor voltage is identical with a node voltage. For example, $v_4 = v_B$. In a similar way, $v_1 = $ _____. A resistor voltage equals plus or minus a node voltage for a (check one):

v_A

(b)

(a) Resistor between two nondatum junctions
(b) Resistor between the datum and a nondatum junction

The diagram below shows a resistor and the datum junction in a network. To see if you know the meaning of node voltage, place on the diagram the symbols v_X and v_Y for the corresponding node voltages, together with reference + and − signs.

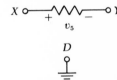

Use KVL to write an expression for the resistor voltage v_5 in terms of the node voltages.

$v_X - v_Y$

$v_5 = $ _____

Suppose the reference for v_5 is reversed. Write an expression for the new v_5 in terms of the same node voltages.

$v_Y - v_X$

node

$v_5 = $ _____

With either reference, v_5 is the difference between two _____ voltages.

The branch voltage of *any* resistor lying between two non-datum junctions equals the difference between two node voltages. _____ (true/false)

True

We now return to the example discussed in the preceding section, the circuit for which is redrawn below. Also given are the equations that resulted from applying KCL at the two non-datum junctions, followed by the use of Ohm's law.

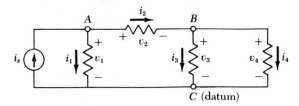

$$G_1 v_1 + G_2 v_2 = i_s$$
$$- G_2 v_2 + G_3 v_3 + G_4 v_4 = 0$$

Expressions for v_1 and v_2 in terms of node voltages were previously established. Write them again here.

(a) v_A

(b) v_B

(a) $v_1 = $ _____

(b) $v_4 = $ _____

Express the other two resistor voltages in terms of node voltages.

(a) $v_A - v_B$

(b) v_B

(a) $v_2 = $ _____

(b) $v_3 = $ _____

Now insert the last four expressions for the resistor voltages into the above KCL equations.

$$G_1 v_A + G_2 (v_A - v_B) = i_s$$
$$- G_2 (v_A - v_B) + G_3 v_B + G_4 v_B$$
$$= 0$$

_____

_____

two

In these two equations there are _____ (how many?) unknowns.

can

If two simultaneous linear equations in two unknowns are independent, they _____ (can/cannot) be solved for the unknowns.

27 COMBINING STEPS WHEN WRITING NODE EQUATIONS

The equations that result from the procedure outlined in the last section are called *node equations*. According to this procedure, after selecting a datum junction and assigning a set of load references to each resistor branch, the following three steps are taken:

(a) Write a KCL equation at each junction except _____ _____. Preferably use the same junction reference, "away," for each junction.

(b) Use Ohm's law to express each resistor current in terms of the corresponding resistor voltage.

(c) Express resistor voltages in terms of _____ voltages. In a network having N_j junctions, the number of node equations equals _____

To see how these steps can be combined, first look at the tabulation given below of the three steps:

Junction A

$$i_2 + i_1 = i_s \qquad \text{Step (a)}$$
$$G_2 v_2 + G_1 v_1 = i_s \qquad \text{Step (b)}$$
$$G_2(v_A - v_B) + G_1 v_A = i_s \qquad \text{Step (c)}$$

Junction B

$$-i_2 + i_3 + i_4 = 0 \qquad \text{Step (a)}$$
$$-G_2 v_2 + G_3 v_3 + G_4 v_4 = 0 \qquad \text{Step (b)}$$
$$-G_2(v_A - v_B) + G_3 v_B + G_4 v_B = 0 \qquad \text{Step (c)}$$

Our objective is to systematize the process represented by each sequence of three equations. But first we observe that the use of a *fixed* reference for i_2 causes the appearance of negative signs in one set of equations. The negative signs in the equations for junction B could be avoided by choosing the orientation of i_2 _____ (toward/away from) junction B. Write a new set of three equations for junction B, using changed references for i_2 and v_2.

_____

_____

_____

Is the last equation of the above set the same as the last equation of the original set? _____. As far as the equation in node voltages is concerned, does the choice of branch references make any difference? _____

the datum junction

node

$N_j - 1$

away from

First term of former junction B equation $G_2(v_B - v_A)$

Yes

No

Thus, by giving up the requirement of having a fixed reference for each branch, equations having all plus signs can be written at *each* junction; that is, assuming the junction reference is "away," plus signs will be obtained if all branch references used *temporarily* for that junction are _____.
When this is done, however, it must be noted that i_2 (in this case) has a different meaning in the equations for the two junctions. These comments do not apply to source references.

away

Having agreed to use "away" for all branch references when writing an equation for a given junction, we shall now discuss an approach that will combine the steps of inserting Ohm's law [step (b)] and expressing resistor branch voltages in terms of node voltages [step (c)] with the writing of KCL [step (a)].

Refer to the diagram of a subnetwork below. A node equation is to be written at junction B. It is agreed to take the cur-

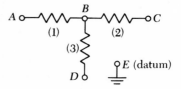

rent reference of branch (1) to be from junction _____ to junction _____. Similarly, the reference of the other two branch currents will be:

B

A

Branch (2): from _____ to _____

B; C

Branch (3): from _____ to _____

B; D

Again, it is agreed to use load sets for references. Therefore, the voltage references are chosen in such a way that, using double subscript notation, the voltage of branch (1) equals _____. Use double subscript notation for the other voltages also and write an equation combining the first two steps in the procedure, namely, KCL followed by Ohm's law, to give an equation in branch voltages and conductances.

v_{BA}

$G_1 v_{BA} + G_2 v_{BC} + G_3 v_{BD} = 0$

Steps (a) and (b): _____

But in terms of node voltages,

$v_B - v_A$

$v_B - v_C$

$v_B - v_D$

$v_{BA} = $ _____

$v_{BC} = $ _____

$v_{BD} = $ _____

Finally, after inserting these into the preceding equation, the node equation will be

$G_1(v_B - v_A) + G_2(v_B - v_C)$
$+ G_3(v_B - v_D) = 0$

Step (c): _____

It now becomes clear how this last equation can be immediately written from the diagram. We can perform steps (a) and (b) mentally. As an example, for the current in branch (1) the process is:

Think "current leaving B through branch (1)"; then think "$G_1 v_{BA}$"; then write $G_1(v_B - v_A)$.

Similarly, for the other two currents in the present illustration,

current leaving through (2)

$G_2 v_{BC}$; $G_2(v_B - v_C)$

(2) Think "_____";
then think "_____"; then write _____

current leaving through (3)

$G_3 v_{BD}$; $G_3(v_B - v_D)$

(3) Think "_____";
then think "_____"; then write _____

As a further example, consider the subnetwork shown below. Write node equations for junctions A and B directly in terms of node voltages, using the above "think-think-write" process.

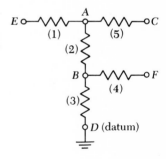

$G_1(v_A - v_E) + G_2(v_A - v_B)$
$+ G_5(v_A - v_C) = 0$

A: _____

$G_2(v_B - v_A) + v_3 v_B$
$+ G_4(v_B - v_F) = 0$

B: _____

When the "think-think-write" procedure is used and no parentheses are removed, each term in the equations has a

plus

_____ sign.

28 EXERCISES IN WRITING NODE EQUATIONS

In the following network the numbers shown are numerical values of resistance in ohms. Choose junction D as the datum.

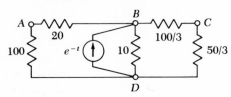

At junction A, the current leaving through the 100-ohm resistor (obtained in one step) is $0.01v_A$; the current leaving through the 20-ohm resistor is $0.05\,(v_A - v_B)$. So the node equation is

Junction A: $0.01v_A + 0.05(v_A - v_B) = 0$

Write the node equations at the other two junctions directly in terms of node voltages in the same way.

Junction B: _____

$-e^{-t} + 0.05\,(v_B - v_A)$
$+ 0.1\,v_B + 0.03\,(v_B - v_C) = 0$

Junction C: _____

$0.03\,(v_C - v_B) + 0.06v_C = 0$

When the terms in these three equations are collected, the result is

$$0.06\,v_A - 0.05\,v_B = 0$$
$$-0.05\,v_A + 0.18\,v_B - 0.03\,v_C = e^{-t}$$
$$-0.03\,v_B + 0.09\,v_C = 0$$

These are three simultaneous algebraic equations, called the _____ equations. The unknowns are called the _____. Each resistor voltage in the network _____ (can/cannot) be expressed in terms of the node voltages.

node

node voltages

can

Write a set of node equations for the network below, with junction (4) as the datum, directly in terms of node voltages.

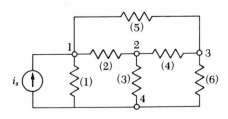

$$G_1 v_1 + G_2(v_1 - v_2)$$
$$+ G_5(v_1 - v_3) = i_s$$
$$G_2(v_2 - v_1) + G_3 v_2$$
$$+ G_4(v_2 - v_3) = 0$$
$$G_4(v_3 - v_2) + G_5(v_3 - v_1)$$
$$+ G_6 v_3 = 0$$

29   VOLTAGE SOURCES IN NODE EQUATIONS

No voltage sources appear in the preceding examples. The question arises as to whether any special difficulties are encountered when writing node equations if voltage sources are present. To discuss this question, consider the following network containing a voltage source whose voltage v is assumed to be known. Take C as the datum junction. As before, the

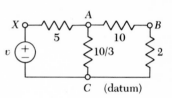

C (datum)

node voltages v_A and v_B are unknown. Is the voltage from the point marked X to junction C known? _____.

Yes

Hence, in this network the number of unknowns in a set of node equations equals _____. Two node equations

two

can be written, those at junctions _____ and _____

$A: B$

The only unusual feature arises with the current *leaving* through the branch from A to X. This equals $v_{AX}/5$. In terms of the source voltage and one or more node voltages this voltage from A to X is $v_{AX} =$ _____

$v_A - v$

Complete writing node equations for the network.

Junction A: _____

$A: \dfrac{1}{5}(v_A - v) + \dfrac{3}{10} v_A$
$+ \dfrac{1}{10}(v_A - v_B) = 0$

$B: \dfrac{1}{10}(v_B - v_A) + \dfrac{1}{2} v_B = 0$

Junction B: _____

How many unknowns are there in these equations? _____

Two

Although the voltage source seems to introduce an additional junction, the voltage at this junction is known. Should the junction be counted for the purpose of writing node equations?

No

In order to solve the network below, how many node equations will be required? _____. Write the required number of node equations and solve for the unknowns in these equations.

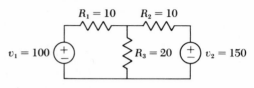

Now find the power *supplied* by the 150-volt source.

The power supplied by v_1 equals: _____

Another approach that can be used in writing node equations when a voltage source is present in a network is to convert a voltage source and series resistor to an *i*-source equivalent. In the first network of this section, suppose that the combination of the voltage source and the 5-ohm resistor is converted to a current source equivalent. Draw the resulting network and write a set of node equations, taking the same datum junction as before.

A: _____

B: _____

Compare with the equations found previously. _____

Carry out the same procedure on the second network considered in this section. After both voltage sources (with their series resistors) are converted to i-source equivalents, the

parallel

result is a _____ circuit. Write the resulting equation; you should get the same result as before.

30 MORE ON VOLTAGE SOURCES (OPTIONAL)

In each of the examples in the last section dealing with the problem of writing node equations for a network containing voltage sources, one terminal of the voltage source is chosen as the datum. If neither terminal of a voltage source is the datum, no serious problems are introduced, but a little more care is required in writing node equations.

An illustration is given in the following network. Suppose a

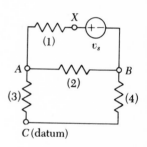

node equation is to be written at junction A. Branches (2) and (3) cause no new problems. The current leaving junction A through branch (1) will equal $G_1 v_{AX}$, and $v_{AX} = v_A - v_{XC}$. But $v_{XC} = v_s + v_B$. Hence, combining these

$v_A - v_s - v_B$

$v_{AX} = $ _____

$G_1(v_A - v_B - v_s)$

Finally, the term contributed by branch (1) to the node equation at junction A is _____

Now repeat this process and find the term contributed to the node equation at junction B by branch (1).

$G_1 v_{XA} = G_1(v_s + v_B - v_A)$

_____

31 INTRODUCTION TO LOOP EQUATIONS

When confronted with the task of writing a set of node equations, the first step is to find a set of voltage variables in terms of which all the resistor voltages can be expressed. In all the examples treated above, the number of variables in the set of

node voltages is ———————— (the same as/fewer than) the
number of resistor branch voltages.

An alternative approach is to apply the basic laws (Ohm's
law and Kirchhoff's laws) in a different order. This time, the
basic scheme is to find a set of *currents* in terms of which all
resistor currents can be expressed.

To illustrate the procedure, consider the following network
which contains four resistors and a voltage source. What is

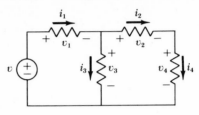

the *total* number of unknowns in this network? ————————

As a first step, write KVL equations in terms of the branch
voltages shown on the diagram around the left- and right-hand
loops, say, in a clockwise orientation.

_____

_____

It is a simple matter to use Ohm's law to substitute for resistor
voltages in terms of resistor currents. Look at the diagram, and
state the type of references chosen for the resistors. ————————.
When Ohm's law is used, the preceding equations become

$$R_1 i_1 + R_3 i_3 = v$$
$$R_2 i_2 + R_4 i_4 - R_3 i_3 = 0$$

The number of unknowns in these two equations is ————————.
This number must be reduced to be the same as the number of
equations if a unique solution is to be obtained.

In arriving at these equations, Ohm's law and KVL have
been used. Use the remaining basic law to express i_3 and i_4
in terms of i_1 and i_2.

(a) $i_3 =$ _____

(b) $i_4 =$ _____

With these substitutions, the previous pair of equations becomes:

_____

_____

The terms of these equations can be collected to yield

$$(R_1 + R_3)i_1 - R_3 i_2 = v$$
$$- R_3 i_1 + (R_2 + R_3 + R_4)i_2 = 0$$

In these two equations there are _____ unknowns. Algebraic methods can therefore be used to find a solution for the unknowns.

two

The procedure for writing the equations described here consists of the following steps.

(a) Write KVL equations in terms of voltages around the internal loops of the network. (This will be clarified shortly.)

(b) Use Ohm's law to express the resistor voltages in terms of their currents.

(c) By applying KCL at the junctions, express all resistor currents in terms of a set of currents which in number is _____ (the same as/smaller than) the number of resistors.   The resulting equations are called *loop equations*.

smaller than

The selection of the set of currents in step (c) is not so simple as the corresponding process when writing node equations, which consists of picking a datum junction and defining node voltages. We shall now proceed to discuss the selection of this set of currents.

32 SELECTING THE CURRENT VARIABLES

The diagram in the preceding section is repeated below. Previously, i_1 and i_2 were chosen as the current variables in terms of which the other currents were expressed. Suppose, now, that i_1 and i_3 are chosen. Use KCL to express i_2 and i_4 in terms of these.

(a) $i_1 - i_3$

(b) $i_1 - i_3$

(a) $i_2 = $ _____

(b) $i_4 = $ _____

Alternatively, choose i_2 and i_3; express i_1 and i_4 in terms of these

(a) $i_2 + i_3$

(b) i_2

(a) $i_1 = $ _____

(b) $i_4 = $ _____

Thus, more than one choice of two currents can be made as the *basis* for expressing all the branch currents. Whichever ones are chosen are called *basis currents*.

In the following diagram, it is anticipated that i_1, i_2, and i_3 can serve as a set of basis currents. Express the remaining

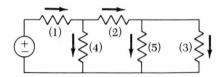

ones in terms of these.

(a) $i_1 - i_2$

(b) $i_2 - i_3$

(a) $i_4 =$ _____

(b) $i_5 =$ _____

This time, choose i_2, i_3, and i_4 as a basis set. Then

(a) $i_2 + i_4$

(b) $i_2 - i_3$

(a) $i_1 =$ _____

(b) $i_5 =$ _____

Try i_1, i_2, and i_4 as a basis set; then

Can't be done

(a) $i_3 =$ _____

(b) $i_5 =$ _____

Examine the diagram. Is there an equation relating i_1, i_2, and

Yes

No

i_4? _____. Are these three currents independent of each other? _____

It appears from this example that a set of currents cannot serve as a basis set if one of the currents in the set can be expressed in terms of the others. In other words, if a set of cur-

independent

rents is to serve as a basis set, it must be _____ (dependent/independent). A further discussion of this question, for the general case, is given in the next section.

The preceding discussion shows that there are many possible basis sets of currents. For a given network, if the right *number* of currents is picked (check one):

(b)

(a) Any combination of this number of currents will constitute a basis set.

(b) Not all combinations of this number of currents will constitute a basis set.

In the network below, express all resistor currents in terms of the basis currents specified.

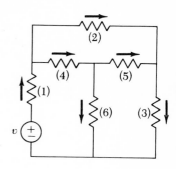

Basis i_1, i_2, i_3

$i_4 =$ _____

$i_5 =$ _____

$i_6 =$ _____

Basis i_3, i_4, i_5

$i_2 =$ _____

$i_1 =$ _____

$i_6 =$ _____

$i_1 - i_2;\quad i_3 - i_5$

$i_3 - i_2;\quad i_3 + i_4 - i_5$

$i_1 - i_3;\quad i_4 - i_5$

The set of three currents $\{i_1, i_2, i_4\}$ cannot constitute a set of basis currents because they are related by KCL at a junction.

Find three other sets of three currents that cannot constitute a basis set.

_____

_____

_____

$\{i_1, i_3, i_6\}$

$\{i_2, i_3, i_5\}$

$\{i_1, i_3, i_6\}$

33 THE NUMBER OF CURRENTS IN A BASIS SET
(REMARK)

In the two preceding sections it has been illustrated that a complete solution for all resistor currents in a network can be obtained by solving a set of simultaneous equations in a small number of current variables which constitute a *basis set* of currents. No general idea was provided as to how to determine, for a given network, the specific number of currents needed in a basis set. A brief discussion of this problem will be provided here.

First, note that a similar question is involved when the variables are voltages. However, in a network having N_j junctions, it is quite simple to see that the number of node voltages is $N_j - 1$ and that any branch voltage can always be written in terms of these $N_j - 1$ node voltages. The present case, however, is slightly more complicated.

We shall limit our consideration to networks in which each source is *accompanied*; that is, there is a resistor in series with each voltage source and there is a resistor in parallel with each current source. We shall not count as a junction of the network the connection point between a voltage source and its series resistor. This amounts to considering a voltage source and its accompanying series resistor as a single branch.

For notational convenience, let the number of junctions in a network be $n + 1$ and the number of resistor branches b. At each junction a KCL equation, which gives a relationship among branch currents, can be written. Of the $n + 1$ such equations, exactly n are independent, as mentioned when discussing node equations. From each independent KCL equation, one of the resistor branch currents can be expressed in terms of other branch currents. Thus, contemplating all the resistor currents as a group, we see that n of them can be eliminated leaving only $b - n$ resistor currents in terms of which all resistor currents can be expressed. Hence, *the number of currents in a basis set is* $b-n$; that is, the number of resistors minus one less than the number of junctions.

Knowing the number of currents in a basis set does not help decide which of the b resistor currents should be grouped to form a basis set. If a set of currents $b - n$ in number is put forward as a candidate to be a basis set, a test for accepting or rejecting the claim is to see if there is any relationship among any of these currents. If one of the currents, say i_x, in the candidate set can be expressed in terms of some of the others, then i_x can be eliminated from the set. The number of remaining currents will no longer equal $b - n$ and, hence, the candidate set of currents can not be a basis set. It is clear from this discussion that the currents in a basis set must *necessarily* be independent; that is, there should be no equation relating any of them. That this condition is *sufficient*, namely, that any set of $b - n$ currents that are independent constitute a basis set, will not be proved here, but it is true.

In the next section, a procedure for picking a basis set of currents will be discussed.

34 MESH CURRENTS

A number of different systematic ways can be established for selecting a basis set of currents. We shall limit ourselves here to one such procedure. This procedure will be illustrated by a previously discussed network, which is redrawn below with the addition of three curved arrows representing fictitious circulating currents called *mesh currents*.

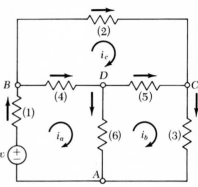

A *mesh* in a network is defined as a closed loop which does not enclose any branch in its interior. The loop $ADBCA$ of the above network has been redrawn below. Branch (5) _____ (lies/does not lie) within this contour. Hence, this loop _____ (is/is not) a mesh. By similar reasoning, loop $ADCA$ _____ (is/is not) a mesh.

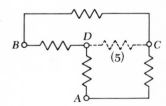

A mesh is, therefore, a particular kind of loop. State whether the following statements are true or false.

(a)   Each mesh in a network is a loop _____
(b)   A loop in a network is not necessarily a mesh _____

Observe that the current i_1 in resistor (1) of the above network is identical with mesh current i_a. Similarly,

i_2 is identical with mesh current _____
i_3 is identical with mesh current _____

The remaining resistor currents can also be expressed in terms of mesh currents. Thus, mesh currents i_a and i_c both circulate "through" resistor (4) but with opposite orientations. The reference orientation of i_4 coincides with that of _____ (i_a/i_c). Hence, in terms of i_a and i_c, $i_4 =$ _____. Write similar expressions for i_5 and i_6 in terms of mesh currents.

(a) $i_5 =$ _____

(b) $i_6 =$ _____

All resistor currents in this network were expressed in terms of the mesh currents. Is there any relationship among the mesh currents? _____. The mesh currents _____.

_____ (constitute/do not constitute) a basis set of currents.

As another illustration, consider the network below in which a set of _____ currents is represented by the curved arrows. Express each resistor current in terms of these currents.

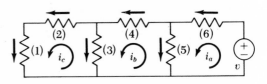

(a) $i_1 =$ _____

(b) $i_2 =$ _____

(c) $i_3 =$ _____

(d) $i_4 =$ _____

(e) $i_5 =$ _____

(f) $i_6 =$ _____

The mesh currents are seen to be a set of circulating currents, one in each mesh of a network. This scheme for selecting a basis set of currents can be applied, therefore, whenever a network can be drawn in such a way that meshes can be identified.

35 NONPLANAR NETWORKS (REMARK)

Meshes can always be identified in any *planar network*, by which is meant any network that can be drawn on a plane without any branches crossing. The simplest network which is *nonplanar* will be illustrated with the use of the following diagram.

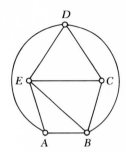

The lines here are not short circuits but represent branches of resistors and sources; they are drawn this way to avoid clutter. As it stands, no branches cross and meshes can be identified.

Now suppose another branch is to be added between junctions A and C. This cannot be done without one branch crossing another, no matter how the branches may be stretched and curved. (Try it.) This new network will therefore be *nonplanar*.

For a nonplanar network it is still possible to write a set of loop equations, but with a basis set of currents other than mesh currents. Mesh currents cannot be defined for a nonplanar network. We shall not deal with nonplanar networks in this book, as far as writing loop equations is concerned.

36 WRITING KVL EQUATIONS

Once a set of basis currents (or mesh currents, in the present instance) are selected, the next step in the procedure under discussion is to write KVL equations. The question of which loops to select for writing KVL equations, and even how many KVL equations to write, comes up. If the final set of equations is to be solved uniquely for the unknowns it contains, the number of equations in it must be (check one):

(a) Less than
(b) Equal to
(c) Greater than

the number of unknowns.

One answer to the question of which loops to use is to write KVL equations around the *same loops* as the ones which define the mesh currents. Will this automatically ensure that there are the same number of equations as unknowns? _____.

(b)

Yes

It can be proved (but we won't do it here) that these equations will be independent.

After KVL equations are written in terms of voltages, the next step is to substitute for each resistor voltage its value in terms of current, using Ohm's law. But this step is so simple it can be combined with the previous one. Thus, when writing a KVL equation, instead of *writing* a voltage, we *think* voltage but write this voltage as R times i with the appropriate R and the appropriate i. Again we assume a load set of references for each resistor.

The following diagram shows a mesh which is part of a more extensive network. Branch current references are shown,

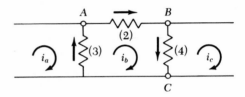

which means that each voltage reference plus sign, although not shown, is imagined to be at the _____ of the corresponding branch current arrow. Starting at A and proceeding clockwise, the first voltage is v_2. We think "v_2" but write $R_2 i_2$. Complete writing the KVL equation for this mesh, thinking "voltage" but writing "resistance times branch current."

$R_2 i_2 +$ _____

The resistor currents can immediately be expressed in terms of mesh currents. Thus,

(a) $i_3 = i_b - i_a$
(b) $i_2 =$ _____
(c) $i_4 =$ _____

The final equation is, therefore,

$R_2 i_b + R_4(i_b - i_c) + R_3(i_b - i_a) = 0$

As previously defined, this is a loop equation. Since the basis currents used are mesh currents, we shall specifically call it a *mesh equation*. Every mesh equation _____ (is/is not) also a loop equation. Every loop equation _____ (is/is not) also a mesh equation.

Notice in this example that the term contributed to the equation by each resistor is preceded by a _____ sign.

This is a result of having chosen the reference orientation for each branch voltage in a certain way relative to the loop orientation; these orientations _____ (coincide/are opposite).

coincide

37 WRITING MESH EQUATIONS DIRECTLY

For convenience, we shall state a number of arbitrary agreements to be adhered to when writing mesh equations.

(a) The references of each resistor branch will be selected as a load set.

(b) The mesh current orientations will all be taken clockwise.

(c) When writing the mesh equation for a particular mesh, the current reference for each resistor on the contour of that mesh will be selected to coincide with that of the mesh current for *that* mesh.

The subnetwork discussed in the last section is redrawn below, but without explicitly shown branch references. With

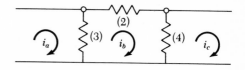

the above agreements, when writing the equation for the center mesh, the reference for the current in (4) is _____ (up/down); the reference for the current in (3) is _____ (up/down). In terms of mesh currents, then,

down

up

The current in (3) = _____
The current in (4) = _____

$i_b - i_a$
$i_b - i_c$

Now suppose an equation is to be written for the right-hand mesh. The reference for the current in (4) will be _____ (up/down). In terms of mesh currents, the current in (4) = _____. This is _____ (the same as/the negative of) the previous expression for the current in (4).

up

$i_c - i_b$;   the negative of

When writing an equation for the left-hand loop, the expression for the current in (3) in terms of mesh currents will be _____

$i_a - i_b$

Branch currents are so easily expressed in terms of mesh currents that the process can be carried out mentally. We again employ a "think-think-write" process for writing mesh equations directly in terms of mesh currents. In going around a mesh to sum voltages, we think "voltage"; then we think "resistance times branch current"; then we express the branch current in terms of mesh currents, when writing the final result.

The process will be illustrated with the "bridge" shown in the following figure. There are _____ (how many?)

three

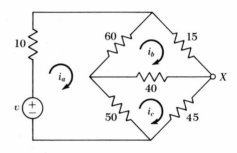

mesh currents. No branch references are shown.

Starting at the upper left, the equation for the mesh defined by i_a is

$i_a - i_c$; i_a

$$+ 60(i_a - i_b) + 50(\qquad) - v + 10(\qquad) = 0$$

Now write the equations of the other two meshes, starting at X in both cases.

$40(i_b - i_c) + 60(i_b - i_a)$
$+ 15i_b = 0$

Upper mesh: _____

$45i_c + 50\ (i_c - i_a)$
$+ 40\ (i_c - i_b) = 0$

Lower mesh: _____

When the terms of these three equations are collected, the result is

$$120i_a - 60i_b - 50i_c = v$$
$$-60i_a + 115i_b - 40i_c = 0$$
$$-50i_a - 40i_b + 135i_c = 0$$

three

mesh currents

mesh

These are three equations in _____ unknowns. The unknowns are called _____ and the equations are called _____ equations.

In the network on the following page, choose mesh currents as shown by the arrows. Write mesh equations directly in terms of mesh currents. (To facilitate comparison of your answers, start at the upper-left corner of each mesh.)

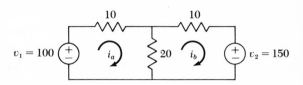

$10i_a + 20(i_a - i_b) - 100 = 0$

$10i_b + 150 + 20(i_b - i_a) = 0$

_____

_____

By collecting terms, these equations can be rewritten as

$$30i_a - 20i_b = 100$$
$$-20i_a + 30i_b = -150$$

Observe that this specific network was analyzed by the use of node equations in Sec. 29. The solution there was obtained by writing a *single* node equation, whereas the solution here requires the simultaneous solution of *two* mesh equations. Anyone interested can solve these equations and then compute the power supplied by each of the sources. Needless to say, the same values should be obtained as in Sec. 29.

In the bridged-tee network below, each mesh current is identical with a certain branch current, assuming suitable choices of branch current references. These currents are

_____, _____, and _____.

Label the mesh currents in the figure accordingly, and then write mesh equations directly in terms of these mesh currents.

$i_1; i_2; i_3$

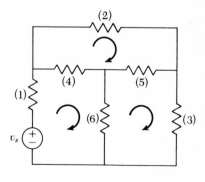

$R_1 i_1 + R_4(i_1 - i_2)$
$\qquad + R_6(i_1 - i_3) = v_s$

$R_2 i_2 + R_5(i_2 - i_3)$
$\qquad + R_1(i_2 - i_1) = 0$

$R_3 i_3 + R_6(i_3 - i_1)$
$\qquad + R_5(i_3 - i_2) = 0$

38   CURRENT SOURCES AND LOOP EQUATIONS

In the examples of the preceding sections dealing with mesh equations, no current sources appeared. The question arises as to whether it is possible to write mesh equations when current sources are present. To answer this question, consider the following network. It may be thought that there are three mesh

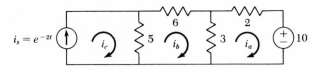

currents, as suggested by the arrows, and that three mesh equations will be required. But mesh current i_c is identical with the current of a _____ (source/resistor) component in the network; it is $i_c = $ _____. This latter current is (check one):

(a)   Known
(b)   Unknown

This means there are only _____ unknown mesh currents.

Equations can, therefore, be written around the two meshes that do not contain the current source. By following the previous process of *thinking* voltage and *writing* resistance times current, write two loop equations around those two meshes directly in terms of mesh currents, starting at the upper left in each case.

source
i_s or e^{-2t}

(a)   known

two

$6 i_b + 3\,(i_b - i_a)$
$\qquad + 5\,(i_b - e^{-2t}) = 0$

$2 i_a + 10 + 3\,(i_a - i_b) = 0$

When terms are collected, these equations become

$14i_b - 3i_a = 5e^{-2t}$

$-3i_b + 5i_a = -10$

Known quantities were transposed to the right. It is now a problem of solving two simultaneous linear equations in two unknowns. The presence of the current source _____ (prevents/does not prevent) the writing of loop equations.

does not prevent

An alternate procedure, which can be used for handling a current source when it is desired to write mesh equations, is to convert a current source in parallel with a resistor to a v-source equivalent. In the preceding network, suppose that the current source and the 5-ohm resistor in parallel with it are converted to a v-source equivalent. Draw the resulting network and write a set of mesh equations taking the same set of basis currents as before.

$11i_b + 3(i_b - i_a) - 5e^{-2t} = 0$

$2i_a + 10 + 3(i_a - i_b) = 0$

Same

Compare with the previous equations. _____

39 UNACCOMPANIED SOURCES (REMARK)

In the preceding discussion of node and mesh equations, it has been assumed that the sources are *accompanied*; a voltage source is accompanied by a series resistor and a current source is accompanied by a parallel resistor. If a source is not accompanied in this way, some modifications must be introduced. For example, if a source is not accompanied, it is not possible to convert to a v-source or i-source equivalent.

As an example (see below) consider a voltage source in parallel with a resistor R. The voltage across the resistor is known,

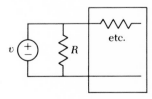

so its current is immediately determined by Ohm's law. The presence of R does not change the voltage v and, hence, does not change the voltage appearing across the network to the right of R. Therefore, as far as that network is concerned, R may just as well be removed. When this is done, the voltage source becomes accompanied and we can proceed.

Another possibility is to have a current source with a series resistor R (see below). With i known, the voltage across R can be immediately found by Ohm's law. The presence of R does

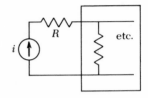

not change i and does not change the current flowing into the network to the right of R. There would be no influence in that network if R were short-circuited. If this is done, then the current source will become accompanied and we can proceed.

A more complicated situation occurs in the network on the left below. The only difference between this and a previously considered bridged-tee network is the fact that the source is

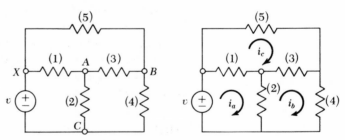

not accompanied. Nevertheless, mesh currents can be defined in the same way as before, as shown in the right-hand diagram above, and the same mesh equations can be written.

In the case of node equations, suppose junction C is selected as a datum. The voltage from the point marked X to the datum is the voltage of the source and is known. Hence, there are only two unknown node voltages and thus we need only two node equations—those at junctions A and B.

Another method is to observe that the network below is equivalent to the original one. By KVL it is clear that there is

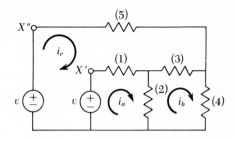

no voltage between the points X' and X'' and, hence, they can be joined together. This common point is the point X in the original diagram. If loop equations are written around the meshes of this modified network they will be identical with the original ones. In this equivalent circuit, however, there are two voltage sources and they are both accompanied by series resistors. Hence, if desired, conversion to i sources can be performed.

Finally, consider the same network with an unaccompanied current source, as shown on the left below. The configuration

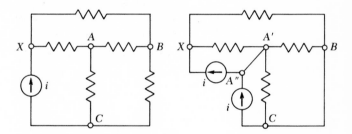

on the right, with two current sources both equal to the original one, is equivalent to the one on the left. To see this, note that by KCL at the point labeled A'', no current flows between A'' and A'. This connection could, therefore, be opened without influencing the remainder of the network. This operation will place the two current sources in series, which is equivalent to a single current source.

With the network on the right, however, the two current sources are accompanied. Hence, conversion to v-source equivalents can be performed, if desired.

40   RECAPITULATION

When presented with a (linear) network containing resistors and sources, two broad approaches have been discussed for determining voltages and currents anywhere in the network. In one of these, attention is focused on a specific branch; the *remainder* of the network is then converted to a simple form by one or more of a number of different techniques, such as, replacing series resistors with an equivalent resistor.   List as many of these as you can think of.

Equivalent series resistance
Equivalent parallel
resistance
Thevenin equivalent
Norton equivalent
Voltage or current divider

(b)

Check one of the following:

(a)   This general approach is good only to find one specific voltage or current.
(b)   This general approach can be used to find all voltages and currents.

The second general approach is to apply the fundamental laws of Kirchhoff and Ohm in systematic ways, in order to arrive at a set of simultaneous equations which must be solved for the unknowns.   Two specific sets of variables were discussed leading to two sets of equations.   They are called:

Variables	*Equations*
(a) _____	_____
(b) _____	_____

(a)   Node voltages; Node equations

(b)   Mesh currents; Mesh (or loop) equations

Once these equations are solved and these variables determined, all other branch voltages and currents are easily found.

Which general approach to use in a given case is answered by asking which requires the least effort.   The answer to this cannot be made in a general categorical statement but is a matter of experience.

Sometimes a combination of these two general approaches is the most beneficial.   In the following diagram it is desired to determine the value of the resistance R such that the power it will absorb will be a maximum, and to determine the amount of that power. For the maximum power to be delivered to R,

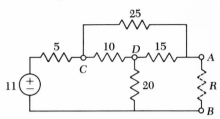

the Thevenin equivalent
resistance of the network

the value of R must equal (in words) _____

_____.

To find this, we must look at the network to the left of AB and

open-circuit; short-circuit

determine the _____ voltage and the _____ current.

Let us initially concentrate on finding the open-circuit voltage. In the diagram, assume that R (drawn dashed) has been removed. We want to find the Thevenin voltage v_e, which equals v_{AB}. Suppose mesh or node equations are the alternatives considered for finding v_{AB}.

Two

How many mesh equations will be required? _____

Three

How many node equations will be required? _____

Let the mesh current orientations both be clockwise and write a set of mesh equations. (Let i_a be the mesh current in the mesh containing the source, and let i_b be the other one.)

$5i_a + 10(i_a - i_b) + 20i_a = 11$

_____

$25i_b + 15i_b + 10(i_b - i_a) = 0$

_____

The solution of these equations is:

$$i_a = \frac{1}{3} \qquad i_b = \frac{1}{15}$$

(You can verify the algebra if you want to.) Now find v_{AB}.

$15i_b + 20i_a$

$v_{AB} =$ _____ (as an expression in terms of i_a and i_b)

$\dfrac{23}{3}$

$v_{AB} =$ _____ (numerical value)

(You may confirm this result by writing a set of node equations instead of the loop equations used here.)

The next step is to find the short-circuit current. The diagram is redrawn below with the terminals short-circuited. If the

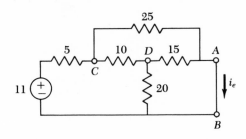

solution is to be obtained by writing mesh equations, how many will be required? _____

Three

Suppose node equations are to be written. How many will be required? _____. Select junction B as the datum and let v_C and v_D be the node voltages. Write a set of node equations.

Two

$$\frac{v_C - 11}{5} + \frac{v_C - v_D}{10} + \frac{v_C}{25} = 0$$

$$\frac{v_D - v_C}{10} + \frac{v_D}{20} + \frac{v_D}{15} = 0$$

The solution of these equations (which you can verify if you wish) is

$$v_C = 7.48 \qquad v_D = 3.45$$

By KCL applied to point A, the current i_e is found to be

$$\frac{v_C}{25} + \frac{v_D}{15} = 0.53$$

$$i_e = \underline{\hspace{5cm}}$$

From the preceding results, the Thevenin equivalent resistance is found to be

$$\frac{23/3}{0.53} = 14.5$$

$$R_e = \underline{\hspace{5cm}}$$

Finally, the diagram is reduced to the one shown below.

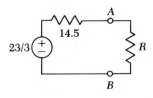

The maximum power will be transferred to the resistor when R = _____ ohms. The value of the maximum power will be P_m = _____ watts.

41 REVIEW PROBLEMS

In this final section, a number of problems will be presented. Some of them are simple and others require a considerable amount of work. In some cases, only an answer will be given; in others cases, some hints for a solution will be supplied for your use *after* you have exhausted your own resources.

PROBLEM 1

In the network below, the current source on the left is to supply 1.5 kw of power. Determine the required value of R.

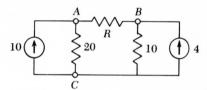

PROBLEM 2

The voltage at the terminals of a laboratory signal generator is measured with a cathode-ray oscilloscope. On open circuit, the voltage is found to be $70 \cos 100\pi t$. With a 200-ohm resistor across the terminals, it is found to be $56 \cos 100\pi t$. Find what the voltage will be with a 100-ohm resistor across its terminals.

14.5

1.013

$p = 10v_{AC} = 10(20)(10 - i_{AB})$

$\therefore i_{AB} = \dfrac{5}{2}$

Replace each source and parallel resistor by a volt-age-source equivalent. The resulting loop equation is

$(R + 10 + 20)\, i_{AB} = 160$

$i_{AB} = \dfrac{160}{R + 30} = \dfrac{5}{2}$

$\therefore R = 34$ ohms

In the Thevenin equivalent:

$v_e = 70 \cos 100\pi t$

$\dfrac{200}{R_e + 200} = \dfrac{56}{70}$

$R_e = 50$

$v = \dfrac{100}{100 + 50} v_e$

$= \dfrac{140}{3} \cos 100\pi t$

PROBLEM 3

This problem seeks to determine under what load conditions (range of load resistance) a real dc power supply can be represented by the voltage source of the Thevenin equivalent (or by the current source of the Norton equivalent) with no more than a stated percentage of error.

(a) A diagram is shown below, in which the power supply is represented by a Thevenin equivalent. Let the error be defined as

$$\text{Error} = \frac{V_0 - V_L}{V_0}$$

Suppose an error greater than 1 percent cannot be tolerated. Determine the minimum value that R_L can have in terms of R_0.

$$\text{Error} = \frac{V_0 - V_L}{V_0}$$

$$= 1 - \frac{V_L}{V_0}$$

$$= 1 - \frac{R_L}{R_L + R_0}$$

$$= \frac{R_0}{R_L + R_0} \leq 0.01$$

$$\therefore R_L \geq 99\, R_0$$

(b) The same supply can be represented by a Norton equivalent, as shown below. The question now has to do with conditions when the power supply can be represented simply by a current source I_0. Let the error now be defined as $(I_0 - I_L)/I_0$.

Determine the maximum value that R_L can have if the error is not to exceed 1 percent.

$$I_L = \frac{R_0}{R_0 + R_L}\, I_0$$

$$\text{Error} = 1 - \frac{R_0}{R_0 + R_L}$$

$$= \frac{R_L}{R_0 + R_L} \leq 0.01$$

$$R_L \leq \frac{R_0}{99}$$

PROBLEM 4

A number of sources are connected in parallel. They are each represented by a voltage-source equivalent as shown in the following diagram. Write an expression for the combined voltage v in terms of the conductances and source voltages.

$$v = \frac{G_1 v_1 + G_2 v_2 + G_3 v_3}{G_1 + G_2 + G_3}$$

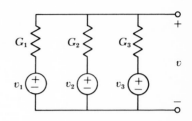

PROBLEM 5

In the diagram below, the network in the box contains sources and resistors. The current through the switch at AB is 100 ma. When the switch is opened, the voltage appearing across the switch is found to be 50 volts. If the switch is replaced by a small resistance (say, 10 or 20 ohms) will the power delivered by the network in the box increase or decrease?

Thevenin equivalent

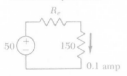

$$R_e = \frac{50}{0.1} - 150 = 350 \text{ ohms}$$

Maximum power when load equals 350 ohms

$150 < 350$, so power $<$ maximum

When 10 or 20 is added to 150 ohms, R will be approaching 350. So power will increase

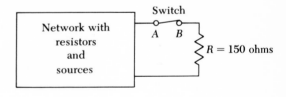

$$i_1 = \frac{2,000}{200} = 10 \text{ amp}$$

$$i_2 = \frac{4,000}{200} = 20 \text{ amp}$$

$$V_1 = 3i_1 + 200 + (i_1 - i_2)$$
$$= 220$$

$$V_2 = (i_2 - i_1) + 200 + 3i_2$$
$$= 270$$

Write mesh equations with
$$R_1 = 0$$

$$R_2 = \frac{(200)^2}{4,000} = 10 \text{ ohms}$$

$$3i_1 + (i_1 - i_2) = 220$$
$$(i_2 - i_1) + 13i_2 = 270$$

New $i_1 = 61$ amp
New $i_2 = 23.6$ amp
Breaker 1 will open.
Breaker 2 will remain
closed.

PROBLEM 6

The diagram below represents a three-wire distribution system. The source voltages are to be adjusted in order to provide the powers shown to the 200-volt loads. The circuit breakers are set to open when there is more than a 100 percent increase in current from rated value (value for the specified loads). During operation, load 1 becomes short-circuited, while the resistance of load (2) remains unchanged. State whether each breaker will open or remain closed.

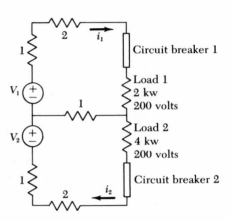

PROBLEM 7

In the bridge network shown below, the load resistance R_L is to be adjusted so that the maximum power will be delivered to it. Find this value of R_L.

We need Thevenin
equivalent R_c. For this,
find $v_{o.c.}$ and $i_{s.c.}$. To
find $v_{o.c.}$ write two mesh
equations in mesh currents
i_1 and i_2.

$$10i_1 + 40(i_1 - i_2) = 12$$

$$40(i_2 - i_1) + 70i_2 = 0$$

$$i_1 = \frac{22}{65} \qquad i_2 = \frac{8}{65}$$

$$v_e = v_{o.c.} = 30(i_1 - i_2) - 50i_2$$
$$= \frac{4}{13}$$

Using any one of a number
of methods:

$$i_{BC} = i_{s.c.} = \frac{12}{850}$$

$$R_e = \frac{850}{39} = 21.8 \text{ ohms}$$

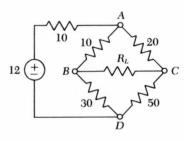

PROBLEM 8

A galvanometer is a low-resistance device that requires only a small amount of current to give maximum deflection. In order to protect it against large currents and to improve its operation, an arrangement of precision resistors (called an Ayrton Shunt) is provided, as shown in the diagram below. The resistance of the galvanometer is $R_m = 100$ ohms. Design a shunt (find values of R_1, R_2, and R_3) which has current reduction ratios (I_g/I_x) of $\frac{1}{2}$, $\frac{1}{10}$, and $\frac{1}{1,000}$.

Ratio is $\frac{1}{2}$ at point A. This gives

$$R_1 + R_2 + R_3 = R_m$$

Ratio is $\frac{1}{10}$ at point B. This gives

$$\frac{R_1 + R_2}{R_1 + R_2 + R_3 + R_m}$$

$$= \frac{R_1 + R_2}{2 R_m} = \frac{1}{10}$$

$$R_1 + R_2 = 20$$

Ratio is $1/1,000$ at point C. This gives

$$\frac{R_1}{2 R_m} = \frac{1}{1,000}$$

Results:

$$R_1 = 0.2$$
$$R_2 = 19.8$$
$$R_3 = 80$$

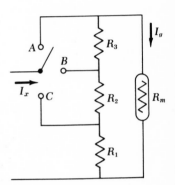

The remaining problems concern voltmeters or ammeters. The basic part of such meters is a galvanometer which consists of a coil able to turn in the magnetic field produced by a permanent magnet. A pointer is attached to the coil so that when the coil turns it deflects the pointer across a scale. In these problems, we shall assume that the meter has a pointer deflection proportional to the current through it. In terms of its effect in a network, the meter can be assumed to be represented by a resistance R_m. A certain maximum current will cause full-scale deflection and the meter current should not be allowed to exceed this maximum.

Voltmeters and ammeters usually have more than one scale, corresponding to different values of current for maximum deflection. For each scale the meter resistance will have a different value. One of the problems of designing a meter is to determine the amount of resistance required for the different scales.

PROBLEM 9

A certain voltmeter has a range of 0–100 volts (see diagram below). It is desired to change it to the range 0–250. The following measurements are made: (a) When the voltmeter is connected to an electronically regulated supply whose voltage is kept constant, the voltmeter reads 75 volts. (b) When a precision 100-kilohm resistor is connected in series with the same supply, the voltmeter reads 50 volts.

Find the value of a resistor R to be placed in series with the voltmeter to change its range from 0–100 to 0–250 volts.

$R = 300$ kilohms
$(R_m = 200$ kilohms$)$

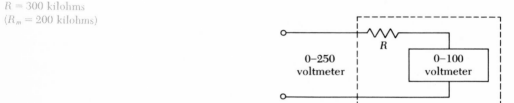

PROBLEM 10

The diagram of a series ohmmeter is shown below. Let I_{FS} be the value of the current in the meter when the pointer gives full-scale deflection. The resistor R_1 (which can include the internal resistance of the battery) is adjustable. To use the instrument, terminals AB are short-circuited and R_1 is adjusted so that full-scale deflection results. When any other resistor is connected to AB, the current through the meter, and hence the deflection, will be reduced. Let R_h represent the value of R_x which gives half-scale deflection, that is, yields a current $I_{FS}/2$.

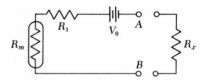

(a)   Determine the value of R_h in terms of V_0 and I_{FS}.

(a) $R_h = R_1 + R_m = \dfrac{V_0}{I_{FS}}$

(b)   Let kI_{FS} be the current corresponding to a general value of R_x, where k is a fraction of full-scale deflection. Determine the value of R_x/R_h in terms of k. Is the deflection a linear function of the resistance to be measured?

(b) $\dfrac{R_x}{R_h} = \dfrac{1-k}{k}$

k is a nonlinear function of R_x.

(c) $V_0 = \dfrac{R_h}{1,000}$

$R_1 = R_h - 25$

(c)   A series ohmmeter is to be designed so that the full-scale current is 1 ma. Assume the meter resistance plus the internal resistance of the battery equals 25 ohms. Determine values of R_1 and V_0 in terms of R_h.

PROBLEM 11

The diagram of a shunt ohmmeter is shown below. It differs from the series ohmmeter in that maximum deflection occurs when the terminals are left open. The meter current for maximum deflection is again labeled I_{FS} and the value of resistance R_x for half-scale deflection is R_h.

(a) $R_h = \dfrac{R_1 R_m}{R_1 + R_m}$

(a)   Determine the value of R_h in terms of R_1 and R_m.

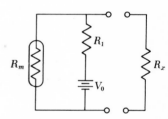

(b)   Let the meter current corresponding to a resistance R_x be kI_{FS}, where k is a fraction of full-scale deflection. Determine the value of R_x/R_h in terms of k.

(b) $\dfrac{R_x}{R_h} = \dfrac{k}{1-k}$

(reciprocal of result for series ohmmeter)

(c) $R_1 = \dfrac{R_m R_h}{R_m - R_h}$

$= \dfrac{100 R_h}{100 - R_h}$

$V_0 = \dfrac{I_{FS} R_m^2}{R_m - R_h}$

$= \dfrac{5}{100 - R_h}$

(c)   It is desired to design a shunt ohmmeter which will have a full-scale current of 0.5 ma. Assume that the meter resistance is $R_m = 100$ ohms and that the battery is ideal. Determine values of V_0 and R_1 in terms of R_h.

PROBLEM 12

The diagram below shows an instrument to be used as a combination voltmeter-ammeter. With respect to the common terminal C, the terminal marked V is for measuring voltages ranging from 0 to V_m; and the terminal marked A is for measuring currents ranging from 0 to I_m. When the current into terminal A is at its maximum value, the voltage across terminals AC is not to exceed V_{Am}. Let the meter current for full-scale deflection be I_{FS} and let the meter resistance be R_m.

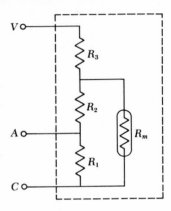

Determine values of R_1, R_2, and R_3 in terms of the quantities V_m, I_m, V_{AM}, R_m, and I_{FS}.

$$R_2 = \frac{V_{Am}}{I_{FS}} - R_m$$

$$R_1 = \frac{V_{Am}}{I_m - I_{FS}}$$

$$R_3 = \frac{(R_1 + R_2)(V_m - R_m I_{FS})}{R_1 I_m}$$

Linear Graphs and Electric Networks

1 INTRODUCTION

Kirchhoff's current and voltage laws are relevant, respectively, to currents in network components which are joined at a junction, and voltages of network components which together form a closed path. These two laws are applicable no matter what particular types of components go to make up a closed path and no matter what types of components are joined at a junction. In order to concentrate on these laws and their consequences, it would be of value to suppress other information contained in a network diagram, such as, whether a particular component is a resistor or a capacitor, or whether it is linear or nonlinear. This is done by representing each component simply as a line segment. The abstraction that results is called a linear graph. The study of the theory of linear graphs is useful because it provides much information about networks and systems, such as, the number of independent equations in a given network, the number of natural frequencies, and the calculations of system functions. This unit will be devoted to a study of the properties of linear graphs. At the outset, it will be necessary to introduce a considerable amount of new terminology whose merit may not be initially clear to everyone. Hopefully, it will become clear before long.

2 DEFINITION OF A GRAPH AND ITS PARTS
(REFERENCE SECTION)

Suppose each component of an electric network is represented by a line segment called a *branch*. The end points of the branches are connected at nodes. A *graph* is defined as a collection of branches and nodes in which each branch connects two nodes. (A single branch or a single node is considered to be a graph, though a degenerate one.) A sequence of branches transversed in going from one node to another is called a *path*. If there exists at least one path from each node of a graph to every other node, we say the graph is *connected*. If not, the graph is *unconnected*. Figures 1 and 2 are illustrations of networks and their corresponding graphs.

A subgraph G_1 of a graph G is a collection of branches and nodes of G such that every branch and node in G_1 is also contained in G. There is no lower limit on the number of nodes or branches in a subgraph; there may be as few as just one or as many as all those in G. A subgraph may be connected or unconnected.

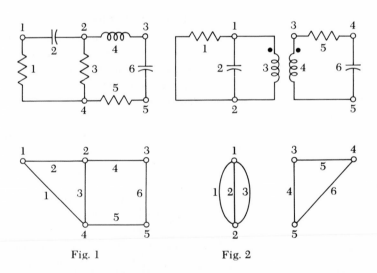

Fig. 1   Fig. 2

In a network, each branch voltage and current has a reference which can be arbitrarily specified. In this program the current and voltage references for a given branch will always be selected in the manner illustrated, with the tail of the current arrow at the plus sign of the voltage reference. This set is called the *load set* of references. With this convention it is not necessary to show both references, since one of them implies the other. In the graph, this single branch reference will be indicated by giving the branch an *orientation* by placing an arrow on the branch, as shown in the redrawing of Fig. 1 as Fig. 3. A linear graph whose branches carry orientations is called an *oriented* graph.

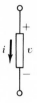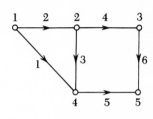

Fig. 3

3 BRANCHES, NODES, AND CONNECTEDNESS
In Fig. 1 of the preceding section, the number of branches

equals _____; the number of nodes equals _____

The following diagram shows two graphs having identical nodes. In the first graph, there is no branch joining node x directly to node y, whereas in the second graph, each node is joined to every other node directly by a branch. The second graph is certainly connected. Is the first graph connected?

_____

According to the definition in the preceding reference section, for a graph to be connected it is not necessary that each node be joined *directly* through a branch to every other node. It is only necessary that there be at least one path going between any two nodes. For each of the graphs in that section, state whether the graph is connected.

(a)   Figure 1: _____

(b)   Figure 2: _____

In Fig. 2 the collection formed by branches 1, 2, and 3, together with their corresponding nodes, is a connected subgraph of the graph. Relative to the graph of Fig. 2, nodes 3, 4, and 5, and branches 4, 5, and 6 form a connected _____ (what kind of graph?)

To *remove a branch* from a graph means to delete the branch *but not the nodes to which the branch is* connected. The first diagram below shows a graph with two branches marked with a ×. In the second diagram, these branches have been removed.

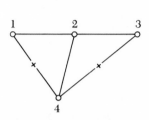

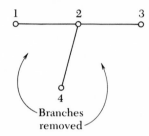

In Fig. 1 of the reference section, suppose branches 1, 5, and 6 are removed. The resulting subgraph is _____ (connected/unconnected). Why? _____

_____

Draw the oriented graph corresponding to the network below, and label the branches and nodes.

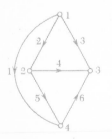

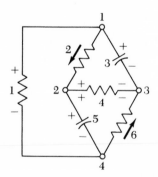

4 VOCABULARY

Up to this point, a number of definitions about linear graphs have been introduced but you may not be sure where it is all leading to. This is typical of the beginning of any subject;

it is first necessary to establish the vocabulary with which the subject can be developed. You are still in the middle of this vocabulary-learning stage.

Give the definitions of the following terms. For confirmation, refer to Sec. 2.

Graph: _____

_____

Path: _____

_____

Connected graph: _____

_____

Subgraph: _____

_____

Oriented graph: _____

_____

5 THE STRUCTURE OF A GRAPH (REFERENCE SECTION)

In a connected graph, there may be more than one path from one node to another. In such a case, it will be possible to start at a node and return to the same node after traversing a *closed* path of branches. We all have an intuitive idea of what a closed path or loop is, but the idea must be made more precise to be useful. Intuitively, if we start at a node, traverse a set of branches, and return to the same node without traversing any branch more than once, we conceive of this as a closed path. To illustrate, look at the diagram on the left below. Starting at node 1, follow the sequence determined by the arrows

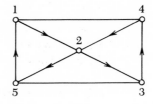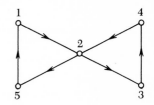

through nodes 2, 3, and 4, back to 2, then to 5, and back to 1. For clarity, the graph is redrawn on the right after the branches not in this sequence are removed. The sequence of branches starting at node 1 and returning to node 1 along the arrows constitutes a path. (Check the definition of *path* to verify this.)

This path is certainly "closed"; but it doesn't fit our intuitive notion of a "loop." By observing the graph on the right, we see that each node has two branches connected to it, except node 2. This observation is made the basis of a definition.

A *loop* is defined as a *connected subgraph* of a graph, which has *exactly two branches* of the *subgraph* connected to each of its nodes. A way of telling if a given subgraph is a loop is to remove *all other* branches from the graph and check to see if the remainder satisfies the definition.

In Fig. (*a*) below, the set of branches {1,4,6} constitutes a loop, as shown in Fig. (*b*). To verify this, observe that this set of branches, together with nodes 1, 3, and 4, form a connected subgraph. (If it seems to you that node 3 has three branches, rather than two, connected to it, you forgot that branch 5 is not in the subgraph in question.) A similar comment applies to node 1.

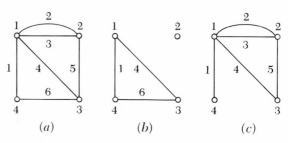

It is possible to remove branches from a graph while keeping the remaining *sub*graph connected. Removal of branch 6 in Fig. (*a*) still leaves a connected graph, as shown in Fig. (*c*). However, if we keep deleting branches, there will come a time when the remainder is not connected.

We define a *tree* of a connected graph as any set of branches which together connect all the nodes of the graph without forming any loops. Thus, in Fig. (*a*) the set of branches {1,3,4} constitutes a tree. In general, a graph has more than one tree. The branches of a tree are called *twigs*. (The concept of tree can be applied only to a connected graph.)

The set of all remaining branches of a graph which are not in the tree, form the complement of the tree, or the *cotree*. The branches of a cotree are called *links*. For the tree {1,3,4} the cotree is {2,5,6}.

6 LOOPS

In the graph shown below, the subgraph consisting of branches {4,5,6} (together with nodes 2, 4, and 5) is a loop because (a) it is connected and (b) two branches of the *subgraph* are connected to each of the nodes. In the following sets of branches, state whether each one does or does not constitute a loop. If any set does not constitute a loop, state why.

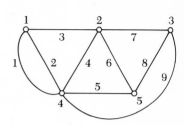

<table>
<tr><td>(a) Loop</td><td>(a) {1,3,4}_____</td></tr>
<tr><td></td><td>_____</td></tr>
<tr><td>(b) Not a loop because node 2 has *three* branches of the set connected to it</td><td>(b) {4,6,7,8}_____</td></tr>
<tr><td></td><td>_____</td></tr>
<tr><td>(c) Not a loop because not connected</td><td>(c){1,2,6,7,8}_____</td></tr>
<tr><td></td><td>_____</td></tr>
<tr><td>(d) Loop</td><td>(d) {2,3,6,8,9}_____</td></tr>
<tr><td></td><td>_____</td></tr>
</table>

Without looking at Sec. 5, define a loop. If you find you need help, read Sec. 5 again; then write the definition without looking back at it.

A loop is (a) a connected subgraph of a graph in which (b) to each node there is connected exactly *two* branches of the subgraph.

_____

_____

_____

(Your definition may be worded differently from the given answer but should contain the two identified ideas, namely, *connectedness* and the existence of exactly *two branches of a subgraph at each node*.)

In the following diagram, branches {1,2,3} together with nodes 1, 2, and 4, form a loop, but node 2 has three branches of the graph (2, 3, and 4) connected to it. Explain why the set of branches does constitute a loop. _____

The definition requires two branches of *subgraph* at each node. Branch 4 is not in the subgraph; only two branches (2 and 3) of the subgraph are connected to node 2.

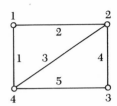

7 TREES

The diagram below shows a graph and one of its subgraphs consisting of branches {1,5,6}; this is a tree of the graph be-

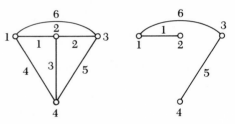

loops

twigs

cause it is (a) connected and (b) contains no _____.
The branches of this subgraph are called _____

Below are shown three other subgraphs of this graph that someone claims are trees.

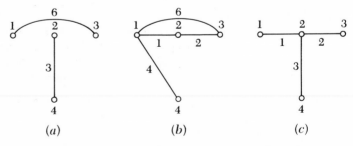

(a)   (b)   (c)

Check those that are trees. If any are not, state why not.

(a)   No; not connected
(b)   No; contains loop
(c)   Tree

(a) _____

(b) _____

(c) _____

link

Branch 4 is not in Fig. (c); this branch is a _____

A tree of a graph is a subgraph. Is its cotree a subgraph?

Yes; No

_____. Is a cotree necessarily connected? _____

In the tabulation below, match the name tabulated under "branch" with the appropriate name tabulated under "subgraph."

	Branch	Subgraph
(a)	Link	1. Cotree
(b)	Twig	2. Tree

Match

(a) 1

(b) 2

(a) and _____

(b) and _____

The diagrams below show a graph and three connected subgraphs which are called _____

trees

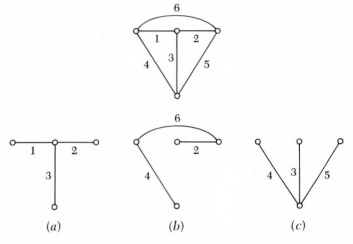

(a)   (b)   (c)

For each of the trees shown above, list the branches of the *graph* which are twigs and those which are links.

	Twigs	Links
(a)	1,2,3	4,5,6
(b)	2,4,6	1,3,5
(c)	3,4,5	1,2,6

	Twigs	Links
(a)		
(b)		
(c)		

twig

Any branch of a connected graph which is not a link is a

_____

Given a tree of a graph, some of the branches of the graph are on the tree and some are not. Name these two types of branches.

Twig

Link

(a) _____ (on tree)

(b) _____ (not on tree)

The set of branches {1,2,3} constitutes a tree of the following graph. List at least five other sets of branches which constitute

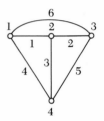

trees. (You may have to draw the trees as an aid.)

{1,2,4}, {1,2,5}
{1,3,5}, {1,3,6}
{1,4,5}, {2,3,4}, {2,3,6}
{3,4,5}, {3,4,6}, {3,5,6}
{1,4,6}, {1,6,5}, {4,6,2}
{2,5,6}, {2,5,4}

_____

_____

_____

_____

_____

Given a graph, someone suggests that each of its branches can be uniquely classified as either a twig or a link. This means that two persons doing it will be certain to arrive at the same classifications. Complete one of the following and cross out the one that is not valid.

(b) Not possible because a branch will be a twig or not only after a tree has been specified. Since there are several trees for a given graph, a particular branch may be a twig for one tree and a link for another. (OES)

(a) The above classification is possible as follows: _____

_____

_____

(b) The above classification is not possible because: _____

_____

_____

Since the definition of a tree mentions nodes, a question arises as to whether the number of twigs on a tree is related to the number of nodes. The graph in the last diagram above has four nodes. The number of twigs in *each* of the three trees shown equals _____

This is an example of a general result which we shall now prove. Let the number of nodes of a graph be N_n and suppose a tree (see diagram below) is to be constructed branch by branch so that each added branch has one of its terminals at an already connected node. The first branch connects two nodes. Can

the other terminal of the new branch be connected to another of the old nodes, or must it necessarily go to a new node not already on the growing tree? Why? _____

_____

_____

Thus, the added branch connects one new node into the growing tree. By continuing this process in which each added branch brings in a new node, and remembering that the graph has N_n nodes, determine the number of twigs on a tree.

Number of twigs = _____

A particular graph has seven nodes; how many twigs will each tree of this graph have? _____

The number of twigs on a tree having N_n nodes is $N_n - 1$, one less than the number of nodes. For convenience, let this number be henceforth denoted by n. Let the number of branches in a graph be b. Write an expression for the number of links in a graph in terms of n and b.

Number of links = _____

Let the number of links in a graph be labeled m. In the graph shown below, state the number of links and the number of twigs.

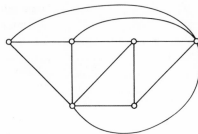

$m = 7$[(number of branches) − (number of nodes − 1)]

Number of links: $m =$ _____

$n = 5$(number of nodes − 1)

Number of twigs: $n =$ _____

Is the following statement true or false?

Once the number of nodes and the number of branches of a connected graph are given, the number of twigs and the number of links are uniquely determined. True or false? _____

True

8   SUMMARY: LOOPS AND TREES

The concepts of loop and tree help to describe the structure of a graph. They are defined as (for comfirmation see Sec. 5):

Loop: _____

_____

Tree: _____

_____

Once a tree of a graph is chosen, the branches of a graph are classified as _____ and _____. Those branches that are not in a tree are in a subgraph called a _____

twigs; links

cotree

Does the concept of a tree apply to an unconnected graph?

No

_____

Is it necessary that a tree be a connected subgraph? _____

Yes

If two people are shown the same connected graph, assuming they will make no errors, which of the following statements are true? Each person will necessarily:

(a)   Identify the same subgraph as a tree. _____

(a)   False

(b)   Find the same number of twigs in a tree. _____

(b)   True

9 REMARK

The theory of linear graphs is useful in many applications besides electric networks. A problem of historical interest, solved by Euler in 1736, was the Königsberg bridge problem. It seemed that a river flowed through the German city of Königsberg and there were two islands in the river. The islands and the two sides of the river were joined by seven bridges, as shown in the diagram below. The citizens of

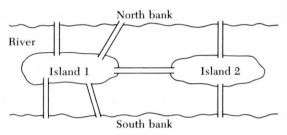

Königsberg liked to take a Sunday stroll along the river and on the islands. They wanted to know if they could take their stroll across all seven of the bridges without crossing any one more than once.

Euler solved their problem by inventing graph theory and showing that it couldn't be done. If the bridges are the branches of a graph of which the nodes correspond to the four pieces of land, the graph representing Königsberg, its islands, and bridges takes the form shown below. The proof consisted

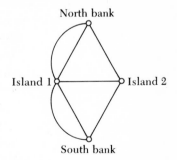

of showing that it is impossible to have a simple path consisting of all the branches of a graph (that is, without retracing any branches) unless exactly two of the nodes have an odd number of branches connected to them. In the Königsberg bridge graph there are four nodes having an odd number of branches.

In depriving the citizens of Königsberg of part of the fun of their Sunday strolls, Euler provided basic knowledge in the field of mathematics which later became important in the theory of electric networks.

10   DESCRIBING A GRAPH

In this section, we shall begin the study of how to describe the way in which the branches of a graph are joined together to form the graph. Eventually we shall deal with the inverse of this operation, which is how to construct a graph if such a description is given.

When a graph is given, simple inspection tells us which branches are joined to which nodes and whether the orientation of a branch is toward a node or away from it. This same information can be given in a concise mathematical form by an array (a *matrix*) in which the nodes of the graph form the rows and the branches form the columns, as shown below.

Branch numbers

	1	2	3 ...
1			
2			
3			
⋮			

Node numbers

The nodes and the branches are both numbered 1, 2, 3, etc. Numbers are to be inserted in the spaces so as to describe how the graph is connected. These numbers are called the *elements* of the matrix.

If a branch is *not* joined to a node, the corresponding element in the matrix is given the value 0. If a branch is joined to a node, it has one of two possible orientations. If the orientation is *away* from the node, the corresponding matrix element is written $+1$; if it is *toward* the node, the corresponding matrix element is written -1.

A simple graph is shown on the following page. How many rows and columns will the above-mentioned matrix have?

Three; three _____ rows and _____ columns.

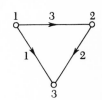

Concentrate temporarily on node 1 of the graph; in the matrix this corresponds to the first _____ (row/column). Branch 2 is not connected to node 1. This means that in the position defined by row 1, column 2 we would place the number _____. Branch 1 is connected to node 1 and oriented away from it; hence, at the position defined by row 1, column 1 we place the number _____. The only other one is branch 3; complete row 1 of the matrix.

In a similar way complete the rest of the matrix shown here, concentrating on nodes 2 and 3 in turn.

Node\Br.	1	2	3
1			
2			
3			

In the preceding, when referring to a position in the matrix we have used cumbersome terminology in saying "the position defined by row something, column something." This can be avoided by using the appropriate notation shown below. Each element of the matrix is designated by the letter a with two

Node\Br.	1	2	3	4 ...
1	a_{11}	a_{12}	a_{13}	a_{14}
2	a_{21}	a_{22}	a_{23}	a_{24}
3	a_{31}	a_{32}	a_{33}	a_{34}
⋮				

subscripts. Look at row 2; the first subscript of each element in row 2 is _____. Observe the pattern of the subscripts in other rows and columns. The second subscript of

column

3

4; 6

2

each element in the matrix refers to the _____ (row/column) that element is in. Element a_{34} is in row _____ and column _____. Similarly a_{62} is in row _____ and column _____.

3

2; away from

2; 3

toward

For a particular graph, suppose $a_{23} = 1$. The information contained in this concerning which branch is joined to which node and how it is oriented is as follows: Branch _____ is joined to node _____ and is oriented _____ (toward/away from) the node. Suppose $a_{32} = -1$; this means branch _____ is joined to node _____ and is oriented _____ (toward/away from) the node.

Complete the table below.

	Branch	Oriented (toward/away from)	Node
$a_{42} = 1$			
$a_{25} = 1$			
$a_{34} = -1$			
$a_{22} = -1$			
$a_{33} = 0$			

2; away from; 4

5; away from; 2

4; toward; 3

2; toward; 2

3; not connected to; 3

11 THE COMPLETE INCIDENCE MATRIX

node

branch

Three; four

The matrix described above is called the *complete incidence matrix*. Each row of this matrix corresponds to a _____ of the graph and each column corresponds to a _____

For the graph shown below, how many rows and how many columns will this matrix have? _____ rows, _____ columns.

incidence

To form the complete _____ matrix, it is possible to focus on the nodes of the graph one at a time and to fill in the corresponding *rows* of the matrix.

The matrix below represents the previous graph; the rows and columns have been numbered. This matrix is called the _____ matrix. The elements in the first row, corresponding to node 1 of the above graph, have been inserted. Fill in the elements for the other two rows.

	1	2	3	4
1	1	0	1	−1
2				
3				

complete incidence

0   1   −1   1
−1   −1   0   0

By inspection, state whether each *row* has the same number of nonzero elements. _____

No

Each row of a complete incidence matrix corresponds to a node of the graph. The number of nonzero elements in a row of any such matrix equals (give a word statement): _____
_____

the number of branches joined at the corresponding node (OES) (Verify this on the above matrix.)

It is also possible to focus on the *branches* of the graph one at a time and to fill in the corresponding _____ of the complete incidence matrix.

columns

When writing a complete incidence matrix, up to this point a table was constructed, with the numbering of the rows and columns shown. We shall gradually eliminate these props and shall use square brackets as shown below to enclose the rows and columns of a matrix.

$$\begin{bmatrix} & & \\ & & \\ & & \end{bmatrix}$$

The graph shown below has been previously considered. Complete the complete incidence matrix, designated by A_a, focusing on the branches one at a time, filling in the nonzero elements first. (First verify that column 4 as filled in is correct.)

1   0   1
0   1   −1
−1   −1   0

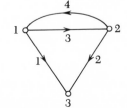

$$A_a = \begin{array}{c} \\ 1 \\ 2 \\ 3 \end{array} \begin{array}{cccc} 1 & 2 & 3 & 4 \\ \left[\begin{array}{cccc} & & & -1 \\ & & & 1 \\ & & & 0 \end{array} \right. & & & \end{array}$$

Yes

Does each *column* of the complete incidence matrix of this graph have the same number of nonzero elements? ________

one

one

In each column, how many plus ones; ________ how many minus ones? ________

Check the appropriate statement below:

(b)

(a) These conclusions just happen to be true for this particular graph.

(b) These conclusions will be true for all graphs.

Give an argument justifying your answer.

A branch in any graph has two ends and can be joined at two nodes only. It must be oriented *away* from one node and *toward* the other. (OES)

____

____

____

12 PROPERTIES OF ROWS OF THE COMPLETE INCIDENCE MATRIX

Adding two rows of a matrix is defined to mean adding the elements of corresponding columns. Let each row be labeled R with a subscript. For example, the second row is labeled R_2.

If $R_1 = [1 \quad 0 \quad 0 \quad -1 \quad -1 \quad 1]$
and $R_2 = [0 \quad -1 \quad 1 \quad 1 \quad 0 \quad 0]$

determine their sum.

$[1 \quad -1 \quad 1 \quad 0 \quad -1 \quad 1]$

$R_1 + R_2 =$ ________

For ease of identification, the complete incidence matrix has been labeled A_a. Each column of A_a of a graph has only two nonzero elements; specify what they are: ________. Suppose all the rows of A_a are added. (This means adding the elements of each ________.) The sum will be a row whose elements equal ________

+1 and −1

column

zero

In the last complete incidence matrix of the preceding section, let the rows be labeled R_1, R_2, and R_3. Using the result immediately above, write the sum of the rows.

$[0 \quad 0 \quad 0 \quad 0]$

$R_1 + R_2 + R_3 =$ ________

Suppose that only the first two rows are known and it is desired to find R_3. Write an expression for R_3 in terms of R_1 and R_2.

$R_3 = -(R_1 + R_2)$

____

Fill in the missing row in the complete incidence matrix below.

$$A_a = \begin{bmatrix} 1 & 0 & 1 & -1 \\ 0 & 1 & -1 & 1 \\ - & - & - & - \end{bmatrix}$$

In this example, the complete incidence matrix has _____ (how many?) rows. If R_1 and R_2 are known, can R_3 be specified *independently*, or is R_3 *dependent* on R_1 and R_2? _____

This means that R_3 can be obtained from R_1 and R_2. Can R_1 be obtained from R_1 and R_3? _____. Can R_2 be obtained from R_1 and R_3? _____

When a matrix has the property described above, the rows are said to be *linearly dependent*; in alternate language, the rows are said to form a *linearly dependent* set.

You have seen that the three-node, four-branch graph under discussion has a complete incidence matrix whose rows are linearly _____. Now consider extending this to an arbitrary graph with any number of nodes and branches. If the rows of the complete incidence matrix are added, each element of the sum will equal _____. The rows of the complete incidence matrix A_a _____ (will be/ will not be) linearly dependent.

Since the rows of a complete incidence matrix are linearly dependent, _____ (*any* one row/only one *particular* row) can be obtained from the remaining rows.

13 THE INCIDENCE MATRIX

The *order* of a matrix is a set of two numbers specifying the number of rows and the number of columns. A matrix having four rows and seven columns is said to be of order 4×7. (The number of *rows* comes first, then the number of *columns*.)

If a graph has five nodes and nine branches, the order of its complete incidence matrix is _____

If a graph has b branches and $n + 1$ nodes, what is the *order* of its complete incidence matrix?

_____

Left margin answers:

$-1 \quad -1 \quad 0 \quad 0$

three

Dependent

Yes
Yes

dependent

zero
will be

any one row

5×9

$(n + 1) \times b$
(Remember: rows first, then columns.)

As a review, write the complete incidence matrix of the graph below.

$$\begin{bmatrix} 1 & 1 & 0 & 0 & 0 \\ 0 & -1 & 1 & 0 & 1 \\ -1 & 0 & -1 & -1 & 0 \\ 0 & 0 & 0 & 1 & -1 \end{bmatrix}$$

$$A_a = \begin{bmatrix} & & & & \\ & & & & \\ & & & & \end{bmatrix}$$

Since any one of the rows of a complete incidence matrix can be obtained from the others and is therefore redundant, it is possible to eliminate any row and still have as much information as before. When one row is eliminated from the complete incidence matrix, the remaining matrix is called a *reduced* incidence matrix, or simply an *incidence matrix.*

If a graph has b branches and $n + 1$ nodes, the order of the (reduced) incidence matrix is _____

$n \times b$

Given a complete incidence matrix, in order to obtain an incidence matrix (reduced) one of the rows is eliminated. This row (check one):

(a)   Can be *any* one row
(b)   Must be a *particular* row

(a)

The *incidence matrix* is given the symbol A, without a subscript. (The subscript on A_a stands for *all*, since all rows are included.)

In the graph below, let the row corresponding to node 3 be eliminated from A_a. How many rows and columns will the corresponding incidence matrix have? _____ rows, _____ columns. Write the incidence matrix A.

Two

four

$$A = \begin{bmatrix} 1 & 0 & 1 & -1 \\ 0 & 1 & -1 & 1 \end{bmatrix}$$

$$A = \begin{bmatrix} & & & \\ & & & \end{bmatrix}$$

Is it true that each column of the incidence matrix has two non-zero elements, a plus 1 and a minus 1? _____ (true/false)

False

The following matrix labeled A is the incidence matrix of a connected graph. The matrix is augmented by inserting an additional row as shown. Place appropriate subscripts on the a's.

$$A = \begin{bmatrix} 1 & 0 & 1 & -1 \\ -1 & -1 & 0 & 0 \end{bmatrix}; \qquad A_a = \begin{bmatrix} 1 & 0 & 1 & -1 \\ -1 & -1 & 0 & 0 \\ a & a & a & a \end{bmatrix}$$

$a_{31} \quad a_{32} \quad a_{33} \quad a_{34}$

If the resulting matrix is to be the complete incidence matrix A_a of the graph, what must be the element values in the added row? _____

$0 \quad 1 \quad -1 \quad 1$

If a matrix is an incidence matrix A of a connected graph, some columns have two nonzero elements (a plus 1 and a minus 1) and some have only one. *Augmenting* the matrix by inserting an additional row can make the resulting matrix an A_a matrix. Which columns of the added row must have a nonzero element? _____

Those columns of A having a single nonzero element (those columns of A whose sum does not already equal zero) (OES)

14   DRAWING A GRAPH FROM AN INCIDENCE MATRIX

The converse of finding the incidence matrix (complete or reduced) of a given graph is to find the graph of a given incidence matrix.

Given an A_a matrix, an appropriate number of small circles can be placed on a piece of paper, to be the nodes of the graph, and they can be numbered in a random manner. Suppose A_a is of the order 4×6. Place the appropriate number of nodes in the space below and label them 1, 2, 3, etc.

(must have four nodes; distribution and labeling arbitrary)

1 ○   ○ 2

4 ○   ○ 3

Suppose the fifth column of the given A_a matrix is as shown below. Place the corresponding branch on the graph and show the orientation arrow.

$$
\begin{matrix}
1 \\
0 \\
0 \\
-1
\end{matrix}
$$

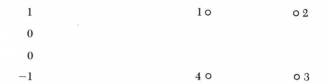

Let the A_a whose fifth column is the one above be the following matrix. Draw the corresponding graph showing the branch orientations. Also number the branches.

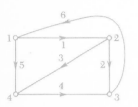

(You may have drawn branch 6 directly from node 1 to node 3 across branch 3. This is OK.)

$$
A_a =
\begin{bmatrix}
1 & 0 & 0 & 0 & 1 & -1 \\
-1 & 1 & 1 & 0 & 0 & 0 \\
0 & -1 & 0 & -1 & 0 & 1 \\
0 & 0 & -1 & 1 & -1 & 0
\end{bmatrix}
$$

(graph nodes 1, 2, 4, 3)

If the given matrix is an incidence matrix (reduced) of order 5×7, the number of nodes to be placed on the paper in preparation for drawing the graph is _____

six

The following is the reduced incidence matrix A of a graph in which the row corresponding to node 5 is omitted. In the first column, corresponding to branch 1, there is a single non-zero element. Between which two nodes will branch 1 be drawn? _____. Draw the graph corresponding to this incidence matrix, showing branch orientations and numbering.

1 and 5

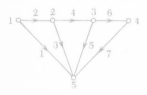

(Your arrangement of nodes might be different.)

$$
A =
\begin{bmatrix}
1 & 1 & 0 & 0 & 0 & 0 & 0 \\
0 & -1 & 1 & 1 & 0 & 0 & 0 \\
0 & 0 & 0 & -1 & 1 & 1 & 0 \\
0 & 0 & 0 & 0 & 0 & -1 & 1
\end{bmatrix}
$$

It is claimed that each of the following matrices is either an A_a or an A matrix of a connected linear graph. For each one, state whether it can be an A matrix, an A_a matrix, or neither.

$$\begin{bmatrix} 1 & 1 & 0 & 0 & 0 \\ 0 & -1 & 1 & 0 & 1 \\ -1 & 0 & -1 & -1 & 0 \end{bmatrix}$$

(a)

$$\begin{bmatrix} 1 & 0 & -1 & -1 & 0 \\ 0 & -1 & 1 & 0 & 1 \\ -1 & 1 & 0 & 1 & -1 \end{bmatrix}$$

(b)

$$\begin{bmatrix} 1 & 0 & -1 & 0 & 1 \\ 0 & 1 & 0 & 1 & -1 \\ -1 & -1 & 0 & 0 & 0 \\ 0 & 1 & 1 & -1 & 0 \end{bmatrix}$$

(c)

(a) A

(b) A_a

(c) Neither

(a) _____

(b) _____

(c) _____

15 DEFINITION OF A CUT-SET (REFERENCE SECTION)

We shall now introduce a new concept which gives a further description of the structure of a linear graph.

By removing certain branches of a graph, a connected graph can be separated into two parts. We shall give the name *cut-set* to a set of branches whose removal causes a connected graph to be separated into two parts each of which is connected. In the figure below, removal of branches 1, 4, and 5 causes the graph to be cut into two parts, as shown in part (b). If branch 2 is also removed, the graph will still be cut into two parts. But should we also call the set of branches {1,2,4,5} a cut-set? Isn't the removal of branch 2 superfluous? To make the definition of a cut-set unambiguous, we must somehow rule out the inclusion of such a superfluous branch. So, to the definition we add the stipulation that replacing *any one of the* branches leaves the graph connected. This rules out set {1,2,4,5}, since replacing {2} leaves the graph unconnected. Thus:

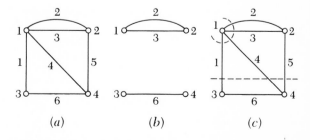

(a) (b) (c)

A cut-set is a set of branches whose removal causes a connected graph to be separated into exactly two parts each of which is connected, with the condition that replacing any one branch of the set renders the graph connected. Each of the parts can contain any number of nodes and branches from 1 on up, limited by the number in the original graph.

A geometrical way of showing a cut-set is to draw a dashed line across the set of branches in question. Thus, in part (c) the dashed lines specify two possible cut-sets.

16   PROPERTIES OF CUT-SETS
If a set of branches is to be a *cut-set*, it must satisfy two conditions. According to the definition, these are:

(a)   Removal of the branches must

_____

(a)   cut the graph into
        exactly two parts

(b)   Replacing any one branch must

_____

(b)   leave the network
        connected

When a cut-set is removed from a graph the resulting graph is _____ (connected/unconnected)

unconnected
(Note that the two
remaining subgraphs
are themselves connected.)

It is easy to check the condition that removal of a particular set of branches causes the graph to become *cut* (or not connected). It is more lengthy to check the condition requiring that replacing any one branch of the set must leave the graph connected, because this requires observing connectedness after replacing each branch of the set, while keeping all the others removed.

In the preceding diagram, it is desired to check whether the set {3,4,5,6} constitutes a cut-set. Redraw the graph with these branches removed and decide whether the *first* condition is satisfied. _____

Yes, two parts; one part
being just node 4

Now suppose each removed branch is replaced one at a time, all other ones remaining removed. The diagram below shows the result if branch 6 is replaced. The graph is now _____ (connected/unconnected)

connected

Draw the resulting graphs when each of the other branches of the set {3,4,5,6} are replaced, all others still being removed.

State below whether they are connected.

unconnected

Graph with branch 3 replaced: _____

connected

Graph with branch 4 replaced: _____

connected

Graph with branch 5 replaced: _____

No

Is the set {3,4,5,6} a cut-set? _____

Give a rule for testing a set of branches to determine if it is a cut-set.

(a)   See if removal of set
      cuts graph exactly into
      two parts

(a)   _____

(b)   Replace one branch at
      a time, checking to see
      if each graph is
      connected

(b)   _____

Each of the diagrams below and on the next page shows a graph in which some of the branches are drawn in dashed lines. It is claimed that each set of dashed branches is a cut-set.

Check any that are; and state why not for any that are not.

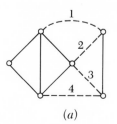

(a)

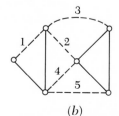

(b)

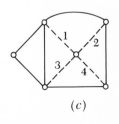

(c)

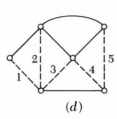

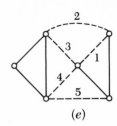

(d)   (e)

(a) _____

(b) _____

(c) _____

(d) _____

(e) _____

For the graph shown below, the set of branches {2,3,4} is a cut-set. List the branches of five other cut-sets.

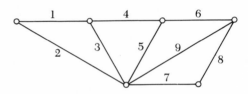

_____

_____

_____

_____

_____

From the preceding, it is clear that, for a given graph, all cut-sets _____ (have/do not have) the same number of branches.

In a graph having five nodes and nine branches, there are (how many?)

_____ branches (called _____) in a tree

_____ branches (called _____) in a cotree

_____ branches in a cut-set

In the following graph suppose all the branches connected to node 1 are cut, as indicated by the dashed line. The resulting

graph will be in _____ (how many?) part(s). This set of branches _____ (is/is not) a cut-set.

Suppose all the branches connected at any one of the nodes in this graph are cut. Each of these sets _____ (will/ will not) be a cut-set. Is this conclusion true for every node of the graph? _____

Let $(n + 1)$, where $n > 1$, be the number of nodes in a connected graph. There may be many cut-sets in the graph but, based on the preceding, we can say that there are at least

_____ cut-sets. The number of cut-sets in a graph can be no less than this number.

In the graph shown below, there must be at least _____ cut-sets. (Insert the largest number of which you are certain without actually finding any cut-sets.)

List all the cut-sets and state whether the number is more than the number you gave above:

(A possible approach is to list all the possible combinations of branches, like {1,5}, {2,3,4}, {1,2,4,5}, etc, and then to eliminate those sets which are not cut-sets. For example, {2,3} is not a cut-set because, after removal of this set, the remaining graph is still connected; {2,3,4,5} is not a cut-set

because _____;

{1,2,3} _____ (is/is not) a cut-set.)

_____
_____
_____

Given a connected graph, a set of branches is a cut-set if and only if:

(a) Removal of the branches cuts the graph into exactly two subgraphs, each of which is connected.

(a) _____

_____

(b) Replacing each branch, with all others of the set removed, results in a connected graph. (OES)

(b) _____

_____

17 HINGED GRAPHS (REMARK)

In the preceding, a general conclusion was reached about branches connected at a node by looking at an example and generalizing. This is sometimes dangerous, because unless all possibilities are considered errors can be made. The question of whether the branches connected to any node of a connected graph constitute a cut-set must be considered more carefully.

A particular type of graph is shown below. When the bran-

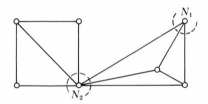

ches connected to node N_1 are cut, N_1 becomes separated from the rest of the graph and the graph is then in *two* parts. This set of branches, therefore, constitutes a cut-set.

Now consider node N_2. When the branches connected to N_2 are all cut, not only is N_2 separated from the rest of the graph, but the rest of the graph is in two parts, making a total of *three* parts. Hence, this set of branches is *not a* cut-set.

Node N_2 is a peculiar kind of node. Every path that goes between a node in one part of the graph to a node in the other part must pass through N_2. Such a node is descriptively called a *hinged node*; a graph containing such a node is called a *hinged* graph.

The answer to the question under consideration then is that the set of all branches connected to a node is a cut-set unless the node is a hinged node.

We shall henceforth exclude hinged graphs from consideration.

18   FUNDAMENTAL CUT-SETS

Given a graph, suppose a tree is selected. Then of all the cutsets in the graph, a few can be singled out and related to the branches of that tree. Figure (a) below shows a graph, and one of its trees is shown at Fig. (b). A *twig* has been marked

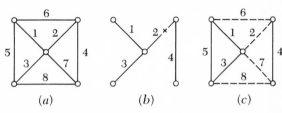

(a)   (b)   (c)

with an **x**. If this twig is removed from the tree, the resulting
subgraph will be in _____ parts.

In Fig. (c), all branches have been replaced on the graph. The ones shown by dashed lines constitute a _____.
How many of these branches are *twigs* of the tree shown in the second diagram? _____

Given a graph *and* one of its trees, each twig will be part of a unique cut-set in which all the branches are links, except for that one twig. Such cut-sets are called *fundamental cutsets* or *f*-cut-sets, for short. For the above graph and the tree shown there, one of the fundamental cut-sets was found to be {2,6,7,8}, the only twig in the cut-set being branch 2.

For the same tree, list the branches for the other fundamental cut-sets and specify the *twig* contained in each.

_____

_____

_____

How many fundamental cut-sets will this graph contain?

_____

How many fundamental cut-sets will any graph contain, in terms of the number of twigs? _____.
In terms of the number of nodes? _____

two

cut-set

One

{1,5,6};   twig: 1
{3,5,8};   twig: 3
{4,7,8};   twig: 4

Four

Same number
1 less

For a graph containing five nodes and nine branches, the
number of fundamental cut-sets will be _____

Is the following definition correct or incorrect?

For a given tree, a fundamental cut-set is a cut-set whose
branches consist of one *link* with the remainder being *twigs*.
_____. If incorrect, what is the correct definition?
_____
_____

The three dashed branches in the graph shown below form a
cut-set. The cut-set was formed without regard to any tree.
Also shown below are three trees. How many branches of each

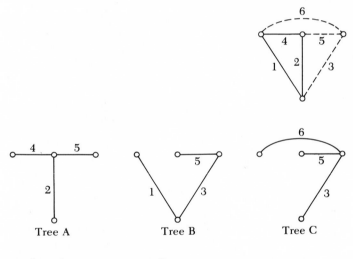

Tree A   Tree B   Tree C

tree does the cut-set contain?

Tree A: _____
Tree B: _____
Tree C: _____

Given a graph, is it first necessary to specify a tree before it
can be decided whether a particular cut-set is fundamental or
not? _____

Is the above cut-set a fundamental cut-set?

_____

Can it be a fundamental cut-set for some tree? _____

For each of the graphs shown below write the *number* of fundamental cut-sets.

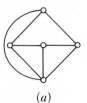 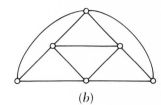

(a)   (b)

(a) _____

(b) _____

The following is a question about your impressions, not a quantitative question. (You might want to find and count the cut-sets of the graphs in order to form your impressions.)

In your opinion, how is the total number of cut-sets in each of the two above graphs related to the number of fundamental cut-sets?

(a) Many less than the number of fundamental cut-sets

(b) About the same as the number of fundamental cut-sets

(c) Many more than the number of fundamental cut-sets

19 AN APPLICATION OF GRAPHS (REMARK)

Other applications that make the study of graphs useful are the analysis of (a) a large-scale network, such as, an electric power network, (b) a communication system that ties together a large number of stations, or (c) a natural-gas pipeline system.

As an example, suppose each station in a communication system is represented by a node and each channel of communication between any two stations is represented by a branch. The channel might be telephone, radio, or even pony express. For a given five-station system, suppose the resulting graph takes the form shown below.

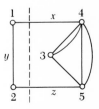

The dashed line shows a cut-set of the graph. If the two channels forming the cut-set are disrupted, stations 1 and 2 can be isolated from the rest of the system. Any tree of the graph will serve to maintain communication between any two stations, and any cut-set will interrupt communication.

The minimum number of channels that must be disrupted in order to eliminate a station is a measure of the "strength" of the communication system. This is equal to the smallest number of branches in all possible cut-sets. For this graph the number is 2. The cut-sets $\{x,y\}$, $\{x,z\}$, and $\{y,z\}$ isolate one or more stations from the system. To strengthen this system (to make it more reliable), it is clear that additional channels should be set up so as to increase the branches in the above cut-sets.

20 CUT-SET ORIENTATION

An orientation can be assigned to a cut-set just as it can to a branch. A cut-set separates a graph into two parts; the branches of the cut-set run between the two parts. In the graph shown below, the set of branches cut by the dashed line $\{1,2,3,4,5\}$ constitutes a cut-set which separates the graph into the parts labeled part 1 and part 2. The orientation of the cut-set can

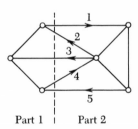

Part 1 | Part 2

be chosen as the orientation either "from part 1 to part 2", or vice-versa. The orientations of some of these branches are directed from part 1 to part 2, while the others have the opposite orientation.

1 and 4

The orientations of branches _____ are from part 1 to part 2.

2, 3, and 5

The orientations of branches _____ are from part 2 to part 1.

Whichever orientation is picked for the cut-set, the orientation of some branches of the cut-set may coincide with it while others may not. For some purposes, it might be desirable to have the cut-set orientation coincide with the orientation of some particular branch of the cut-set. But, *in general*, there is no specific branch with which a cut-set can be identified. However, given a graph and a tree, certain cut-sets are each identified with certain specific branches. Which cut-sets? _____. Which branches? _____

It may be convenient, and it makes some sense, to give a fundamental cut-set the same orientation as that of the twig it contains. We shall henceforth do this. Figure (*a*) below shows a graph, and Fig. (*b*) shows a specific tree. Figure (*c*) shows a

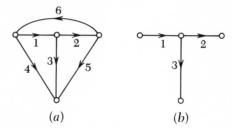

(*a*)   (*b*)

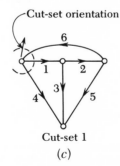
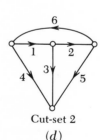
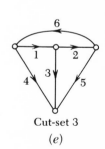

Cut-set orientation

Cut-set 1   Cut-set 2   Cut-set 3

(*c*)   (*d*)   (*e*)

dashed line representing a fundamental cut-set containing twig 1 of this tree; the orientation of this cut-set (numbered cut-set 1) is chosen to coincide with the orientation of twig 1.

Draw dashed lines cutting the branches of the other two fundamental cut-sets shown at Figs. (*d*) and (*e*) for the same tree, and draw an arrow on each indicating the orientation.

Cut-sets that are not fundamental have no special relation to any specific branch of the graph. They have no preferred orientation, so for them an orientation is chosen *arbitrarily*.

Fundamental

Twigs for the given tree

Cut-set 2

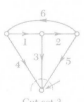

Cut-set 3

(a) This *is not* an *f*-cut-set. The orientation you pick may depend on no more than how you feel at the moment.

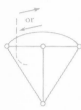

(b) This *is* an *f*-cut-set characterized by twig 6. The orientation is chosen to coincide with that of Twig 6.

The diagram below shows a tree of a graph and two cut-sets, one of which is a fundamental cut-set for the given tree. Put orientations on the cut-sets and give reasons for your choice.

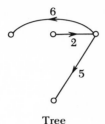

Tree

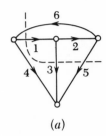

(a)

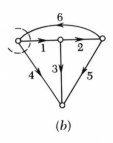

(b)

(a) _____
_____
_____

(b) _____
_____
_____

21 DEFINITION OF FUNDAMENTAL CUT-SET MATRIX

Just as the incidence matrix is used to describe the manner in which the branches of a graph are connected to the nodes, and with what orientation, so also is it possible to introduce another matrix which describes which branches are contained in each fundamental cut-set and their orientations. This matrix is called the *f-cut-set matrix* and is designated by C. Each row of the matrix corresponds to an *f*-cut-set of the graph. The columns of the matrix, as in the case of the incidence matrix, again correspond to the _____ of the graph. The elements of the matrix are labeled c_{jk}, as indicated in the following matrix.

branches

$$\begin{array}{cc} & \text{Branches} \longrightarrow \\ \text{f-cut-sets} & \begin{array}{cccc} 1 & 2 & 3 & 4\ \ldots \end{array} \\ \downarrow \begin{array}{c} 1 \\ 2 \\ 3 \\ \vdots \end{array} & \begin{bmatrix} c_{11} & c_{12} & c_{13} & c_{14} \cdots \\ c_{21} & c_{22} & c_{23} & c_{24} \cdots \\ c_{31} & c_{32} & c_{33} & c_{34} \cdots \\ \vdots & \vdots & \vdots & \vdots \end{bmatrix} \end{array}$$

If a branch is not contained in a particular *f*-cut-set, the corresponding element in the matrix is given the value 0. Thus, suppose branch 3 is not in cut-set 1; which element of the matrix will be zero? ________. Suppose cut-set 4 does not contain branch 2; the element of the matrix which will be zero is ________

c_{13}

c_{42}

If a branch is in a particular *f*-cut-set, it has one of two possible orientations: if the orientation of the branch coincides with that of the *f*-cut-set, the corresponding matrix element is written + 1; if the orientations do not coincide, the corresponding matrix element is written − 1. Thus, if branch 6 is in *f*-cut-set 2 and the orientations coincide, then $c_{26} =$ ________

1

For a particular graph, suppose a tree has been chosen, the *f*-cut-set matrix has been written, and $c_{21} = -1$. What information does this convey about which branch is in which *f*-cut-set and how it is oriented? The answer may be stated:

Branch ________ is in *f*-cut-set ________; the branch and cut-set orientations ________ (coincide/do not coincide)

1; 2
do not coincide.

Similarly, suppose $c_{34} = 1$; this means that branch ________ is in *f*-cut-set ________ and that the two orientations ________ (coincide/do not coincide). Also, $c_{12} = 0$ means that ________

4
3
coincide
branch 2 is not in *f*-cut-set 1

22 PROPERTIES OF THE *F*-CUT-SET MATRIX

For the graph below, and tree shown in heavy lines, how many rows and how many columns will the *f*-cut-set matrix *C* have? ________ rows; ________ columns. Will these numbers be the same for every other tree? ________

Three; seven
Yes

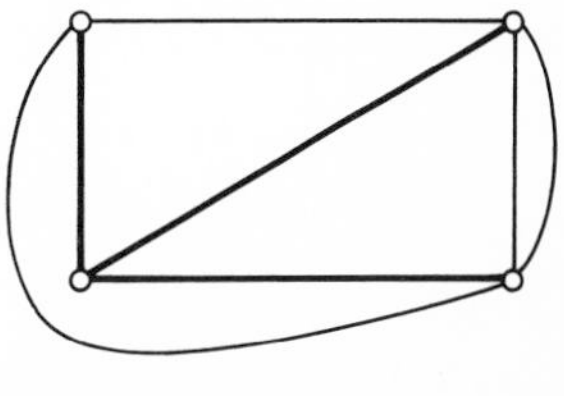

To form the f-cut-set matrix of a graph:

tree

(a)   The first step is to choose a _____

twigs in the tree

(b)   The number of rows of the matrix should equal the number of _____

branches

(c)   The number of columns of the matrix should equal the number of _____ of the graph.

(d)   Then, attention should be focused on the twigs, one at a time; corresponding to the f-cut-set for each twig, the

row

_____ (row/column) of the matrix C should be filled in.

In the graph below, a tree consisting of branches 1, 2, and 3 is chosen, as shown by the heavy lines. The corresponding f-cut-sets and their orientations are represented by the dashed lines. The elements in the first row of the C matrix have been entered. Fill in the elements of the other two rows.

0   1   0   −1   1
0   0   1   0   −1

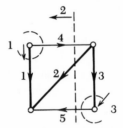

$$C = \begin{array}{c} \\ 1 \\ 2 \\ 3 \end{array} \begin{array}{ccccc} 1 & 2 & 3 & 4 & 5 \\ \left[\begin{array}{ccccc} 1 & 0 & 0 & 1 & 0 \\ & & & & \\ & & & & \end{array}\right. \end{array}$$

No

Does each row of the preceding C matrix have the same number of nonzero elements? _____

cut-set 1

Row 1 in the *matrix* corresponds to _____ in the *graph*. There are two nonzero elements in row 1 of the matrix.

Two

How many branches lie in cut-set 1 in the graph? _____

Each row of a C matrix corresponds to a fundamental cut-set. The number of nonzero elements in a row of any C matrix equals the number of _____

branches in the
corresponding f-cut-set

(give a word statement). Verify this for the last two rows of the preceding C matrix.

For the graph shown on the following page, the tree consisting of branches 1, 2, 3, and 4 is chosen. The corresponding

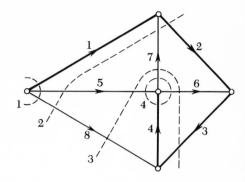

fundamental cut-sets are implied by the sequence of dashed lines. (The orientations of these cut-sets are not explicitly shown in order to avoid clutter.)

Write the *f*-cut-set matrix

$$C = \begin{bmatrix} 1 & 0 & 0 & 0 & 1 & 0 & 0 & 1 \\ 0 & 1 & 0 & 0 & 1 & 0 & -1 & 1 \\ 0 & 0 & 1 & 0 & 1 & -1 & -1 & 1 \\ 0 & 0 & 0 & 1 & 1 & -1 & -1 & 0 \end{bmatrix}$$

$$C = \begin{bmatrix} \\ \\ \\ \end{bmatrix}$$

Observe the number of nonzero elements in each column. Are they all the same? _____

No

In the case of the complete incidence matrix A_a there are exactly _____ nonzero elements in each column, because each branch of a graph can be connected at only _____ nodes.

two

two

If the *C* matrix had exactly two nonzero elements in each column, what would be the corresponding requirement on the branches? _____

Each branch should be contained in exactly two *f*-cut-sets. (OES)

_____

one

Each twig of the chosen tree can lie in _____ (how many?) cut-sets.

Given a graph, to form an *f*-cut-set matrix, first a tree is selected. Each *f*-cut-set contains _____ (how many?) twig(s). A given twig will appear in _____ (how many?) *f*-cut-set(s). The column of *C* corresponding to a twig will have _____ (how many?) nonzero element(s). Verify this on the preceding *C* matrices.

one

one

one

A previously given graph and its C matrix are repeated below.

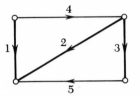

$$C = \begin{bmatrix} 1 & 0 & 0 & 1 & 0 \\ 0 & 1 & 0 & -1 & 1 \\ 0 & 0 & 1 & 0 & -1 \end{bmatrix}$$

Focus on the first column of C. This corresponds to branch 1 of the graph, which is a twig. In this column, there is a nonzero element only in the first row.

In the case of the complete incidence matrix A_a, one of the rows can be obtained as the negative sum of all the other rows, which is equivalent to saying that the rows are dependent. In the case of the C matrix under discussion, no amount of manipulation of the last two rows—adding them or subtracting them, or multiplying them—can cause a nonzero element to appear in the first row. Hence, the first row of this C matrix cannot be obtained as a *linear combination* of the other two rows. Unlike the A_a matrix, then, the rows of this C matrix are

independent

_____

Now consider another previously determined C matrix repeated below. By a similar investigation determine whether or not the rows of this C matrix are independent. They _____ (are/are not) independent.

are

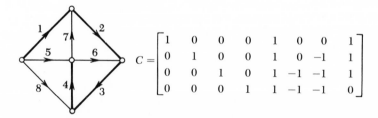

$$C = \begin{bmatrix} 1 & 0 & 0 & 0 & 1 & 0 & 0 & 1 \\ 0 & 1 & 0 & 0 & 1 & 0 & -1 & 1 \\ 0 & 0 & 1 & 0 & 1 & -1 & -1 & 1 \\ 0 & 0 & 0 & 1 & 1 & -1 & -1 & 0 \end{bmatrix}$$

For the general case of any connected graph, with the C matrix formed in the manner described above, is the following true or false: "The rows of the fundamental cut-set matrix of

True

$n \times b$

Same

a linear graph are independent." _____

For a graph having b branches and $n + 1$ nodes, state the order of the f-cut-set matrix. _____. How is this related to the order of the (reduced) incidence matrix A?

_____

23   REVIEW OF CUT-SETS

In the eight preceding sections you have learned about cut-sets. If you need confirmation of any answers to the following questions, review the preceding eight sections.

A cut-set of a connected graph is defined as: _____

_____
_____

Of all the cut-sets in a graph, the *fundamental cut-sets* for a given tree are the most important.   In a graph having b branches and $n + 1$ nodes, there are _____ (how many?) fundamental cut-sets for a given tree.

Given a graph and one of its trees, each fundamental cut-set contains a unique _____ (link/twig).

How is the orientation of a fundamental cut-set chosen?

_____

For the graph shown below, let a tree consisting of branches 1 and 2 be chosen.   Write the C matrix.   Also write the in-

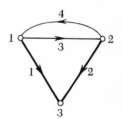

cidence matrix for this graph with node 3 omitted.

24   FUNDAMENTAL LOOPS

The notion of a loop was defined in Sec. 5; perhaps you should reread it before going on.   In this section, we shall consider the properties of loops in a graph and shall introduce a special class of loops called fundamental loops.   You will also learn how to describe the loops of a graph by means of a matrix.

In the graph below, the set of branches {1,3,5,6,} constitutes a loop. There are six other loops in this graph. Specify the set of branches in each loop.

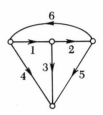

{1,2,6}   {4,5,6}
{1,3,4}   {1,2,4,5}
{2,3,5}   {2,3,4,6}

Is the following statement true or false? "Each loop in a graph need not have the same number of branches." _____

True

Of all the loops in a graph, one group can be singled out and related to the links corresponding to a tree. A graph is shown at Fig. (a) below and one of its trees, consisting of twigs 5, 6, 7, and 8, is shown at Fig. (b). In Fig. (c), a loop has been formed by replacing one of the branches, shown dashed. How many *links* corresponding to the given tree does this loop contain?

One

_____

Suppose branch 4, which is a link, is added to the tree in Fig. (b). List the set of branches of the loop so formed. _____.
This loop has _____ (how many?) link(s).

{4,6,7,8}

one

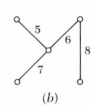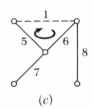

(a)   (b)   (c)

Based on this example, we observe that, given a tree, each link, together with some twigs, will form a loop. Given a graph and one of its trees, we define a *fundamental loop* as one that contains only one link. In the above graph, the set of branches {1,5,6} was found to be a loop containing a single link corresponding to the chosen tree, namely, branch _____.
This loop _____ (is/is not) a fundamental loop.

1

is

For the same graph and the same tree, list the branches constituting the remaining fundamental loops and specify the links contained in each.

{2,5,7};   link: 2
{3,6,8};   link: 3
{4,6,7,8};   link: 4

Four

As many as the links

Six

(a) n
(b) $b - n$
(c) $b - n$

(b)
(a)

five

(a)   none
(b)   none
(c) n
(d) $b - n$
(e)   none

_____
_____
_____
_____

How many fundamental loops are there in this graph?

_____

In terms of the number of links, how many fundamental loops will a graph contain in general? _____

If a graph has six links, how many fundamental loops will it have? _____. If a graph has $n + 1$ nodes and b branches, it will have (how many?):

(a)   Twigs:_____
(b)   Links: _____
(c)   Fundamental loops: _____

Given a tree of a graph, each of the objects listed below on the left defines one of the objects listed on the right. Match them up.

1. Twig   (a)   Fundamental loop
2. Link   (b)   Fundamental cut-set

Match
1 and _____
2 and _____

If a graph has eight branches and three fundamental cut-sets, it will have _____ (how many?) fundamental loops.

A given graph will have a fixed number of branches b and a fixed number of nodes $n + 1$. A number of concepts describing the properties of a graph, such as, tree, cut-set, and link, have been introduced. The number of trees, number of loops, etc., may depend only on b and/or n, or they may depend on how the branches are connected to the nodes, or other such properties.

For each of the following, give an expression in terms of b and/or n. If no such expression has been derived, write none.

(a)   Number of trees: _____
(b)   Number of cut-sets: _____
(c)   Number of twigs: _____
(d)   Number of fundamental loops: _____
(e)   Number of branches in a loop: _____

(f) n
(g) none
(h) $b - n$

(f) Number of fundamental cut-sets: _____
(g) Number of loops: _____
(h) Number of links: _____

For each of the graphs below, state the number of fundamental loops. (Note: the point at the center of b is not a node; the branches just cross over there.)

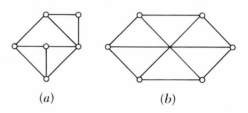

(a)   (b)

(a) Four
(b) Four

(a) _____
(b) _____

If a graph has four fundamental loops and three fundamental cut-sets, it will have a total of _____ (how many?) branches.

seven

25 ORIENTATION OF LOOPS

A loop can be assigned an orientation. When we think of a loop, we usually think of some rotation, or circulation, or traveling around. There are two possible directions for circulating around a loop: clockwise or counterclockwise; hence, a loop can have either of these two possible orientations. A loop orientation is indicated with a curved arrow, as shown in the diagram below.

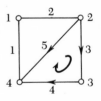

In the diagram, the orientation of branch 4 coincides with the orientation of the loop shown. Specify whether the orientations of branches 3 and 5 coincide with or are opposed to the orientation of the loop.

3: coincides with
5: is opposed to

3: _____
5: _____

Whatever orientation is picked for the loop, some of the branch orientations may coincide with it and some may not. If a loop could be identified with some particular branch, it might be desirable to assign the orientation of that branch to the loop. Although, *in general*, there is no particular branch with which a given loop can be definitely identified, certain loops, called _____, are uniquely identified with certain branches. Which branches? _____

By convention, a fundamental loop is given the same orientation as its defining link. Figure (*a*) below shows a graph, and Fig. (*b*) shows a specific tree. Figure (*c*) shows the fundamental loop defined by link 4. The orientation of the loop is chosen to coincide with that of its defining link.

Add the remaining links to Fig. (*c*), showing the orientations of the remaining fundamental loops for the same tree.

fundamental loops

Links

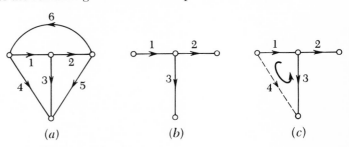

(a)   (b)   (c)

26 PLANAR GRAPHS

Up to this point, no distinction has been made among graphs on the basis of the manner in which they are drawn on paper. In the graph below, the point at the center is not a node. This graph has the feature that no matter how it is redrawn (one redrawing is also shown) it is impossible to avoid having at least two of the branches cross.

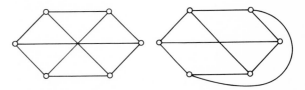

A graph is called a *planar* graph if it can be drawn on a plane in such a way that no two branches cross. It is reasonable to classify graphs as to whether or not they are planar, because planar and nonplanar graphs have certain properties which are different, as will soon be discussed.

The last graph is _____ (planar/nonplanar)

Which of the following graphs are planar and which are nonplanar?

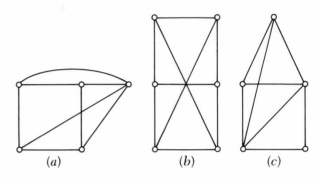

(a)   (b)   (c)

(a) _____

(b) _____

(c) _____

In a graph having five nodes, suppose each node has a branch joining it to every other node. Is this graph planar or nonplanar? _____. (You should draw it and see.)

The planar graph below bears some resemblance to a fish net. The term "mesh" for the little "windows," such as the

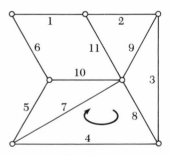

one indicated by the arrow, thus seems appropriate.

In a *planar* graph a *mesh* is defined as a set of branches which forms a loop and which encloses no other branch. The set {4,7,8} is a mesh, since there is no other branch located in the interior or the contour formed by these branches.

Which, if any, of the following loops are meshes?

(a) {1,11,10,6}
(b) {4,5,10,8}
(c) {7,9,3,4}
(d) {2,9,11}

The diagram below shows two renderings of the same graph, which differ from each other only in the position of branch 5.

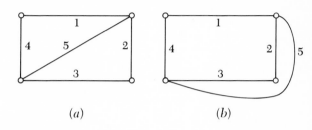

(a)   (b)

List the meshes in Fig. (a) _____
List the meshes in Fig. (b) _____

Are they the same or different? _____

_____

Is the following statement true of false?

"For a given planar graph, whether or not a set of branches is a *mesh* depends on the way in which the graph is drawn."

_____

Redraw the following graph so that the loop {1,2,3,4} is a mesh.

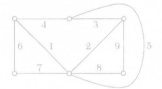

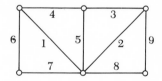

The diagram below shows a graph and one of its trees.

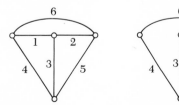

For this tree list all the *fundamental loops.*

{1,3,4}

{2,3,4,6}

{4,5,6}

Is each of these fundamental loops also a *mesh* of the graph,

No

as drawn? _____

For the same graph, choose a tree so that, if possible, the fundamental loops for that tree are the meshes of the graph as shown below. Also, show the orientations of the links.

(Tree in solid lines)

link

For a given tree, each fundamental loop contains only one _____ (twig/link). Since this branch does not appear in any other fundamental loop, the only branches which two

twigs

fundamental loops can have in common are _____

If the meshes of a graph are to be fundamental loops, a com-

twig

mon branch between any two meshes must be a _____ (twig/link)

For the graph below, it is desired that the meshes be fundamental loops for some tree. Draw in those branches which are *required* to be twigs of that tree, on the basis of the above discussion.

 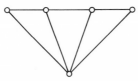

No

Are these necessarily *all* the twigs of that tree? _____

It is desired to determine the possibility of choosing a tree for the graph on the following page, so that the fundamental loops for that tree are the meshes of the graph as drawn. For the given graph, see if you can find such a tree by trial.

I can't do it. _____

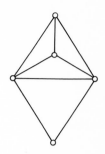

To discover the principle involved here, consider the graph below. Since the meshes are to be fundamental loops, what kind of branches must the ones common to the meshes be?

_____

The graph has been partially redrawn by emplacing the nodes. Now, draw in all of the branches common to two of the meshes. Then try to complete the tree.

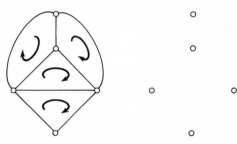

Can a tree be formed that includes all of the branches common to two meshes? _____. Why or why not?

_____

On the basis of the last few pages, complete the statement of the following theorem.

"The meshes of a connected graph can be the fundamental loops for some tree if and only if the set of branches common

to any two meshes _____."

In the planar graph shown below, is it possible to choose a tree such that the meshes are fundamental loops for that tree?

_____

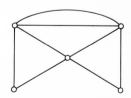

27   FUNDAMENTAL LOOP MATRICES

As you might suspect from the fact that matrices were used to describe the structure of a graph in terms of the connection of branches at nodes and in terms of the f-cut-sets, it is also possible to give a matrix description of the structure of a graph in terms of its fundamental loops (abbreviated f-loops). By analogy with the f-cut-set matrix C, we define an *f-loop matrix B*, each row of which corresponds to an f-loop of the graph and each column of which corresponds to a branch. The elements of the matrix are labeled b_{jk}.

The values of the elements of the B matrix are fixed in a manner analogous to those of the C matrix. If a branch is not contained in a particular f-loop, the corresponding matrix element is given the value _____. If a branch is in an f-loop, it has one of two possible orientations: if the orientation of the branch *coincides with* that of the loop, the corresponding matrix element is written _____; if *opposite,* _____

In a particular B matrix, it is found that $b_{23} = 1$. This means that branch _____ is in f-loop _____ and that their orientations _____ (coincide/do not coincide). Similarly,

$b_{11} = 0$ means that _____

$b_{53} = -1$ means that _____

_____

If a graph has nine branches and four links, how many rows and how many columns will the f-loop matrix B have? _____ rows; _____ columns.

For the graph shown below, how many rows and how many columns will the f-loop matrix B have? _____ rows; _____ columns.

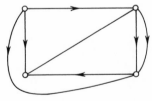

If a graph has b branches and $n + 1$ nodes, what is the order of the f-loop matrix? _____

Margin answers (left column):

0

$+1$
-1

3; 2

coincide

branch 1 is not in f-loop 1

branch 3 is in f-loop 5; their orientations do not coincide

Four
nine

Four
seven

$(b - n) \times b$

To form the *f*-loop matrix of a graph, the first step is to choose a tree. Attention is then focused on the links one at a time. The row of *B* corresponding to the *f*-loop for each link is then filled in.

In the graph shown below, a tree consisting of branches 1, 2, 3, and 4 is chosen, as shown by the heavy lines. The links are branches 5, 6, and 7. The fundamental loops defined by these links are shown by the curved arrows. The elements of the first row of the *B* matrix have been entered.

Fill in the elements of the other rows.

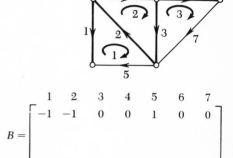

$$B = \begin{array}{ccccccc} 1 & 2 & 3 & 4 & 5 & 6 & 7 \\ \left[\begin{array}{ccccccc} -1 & -1 & 0 & 0 & 1 & 0 & 0 \end{array}\right. \end{array}$$

$$\begin{array}{ccccccc} 0 & 1 & 1 & 0 & 0 & 1 & 0 \\ 0 & 0 & -1 & 1 & 0 & 0 & 1 \end{array}$$

One possibility is:

$$B = \begin{bmatrix} 1 & 0 & 1 & 1 & 0 & 0 \\ -1 & -1 & 0 & 0 & 1 & 0 \\ 0 & -1 & 1 & 0 & 0 & 1 \end{bmatrix}$$

No

one

For the graph below, choose a tree for which the meshes are *f*-loops and write the *B* matrix.

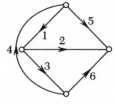

$$B = \begin{bmatrix} & & & & & \\ & & & & & \end{bmatrix}$$

Observe the number of nonzero elements in each column. Are they the same? _____

When discussing the *f-cut-set* matrix *C*, it was observed that each twig appears in exactly one *f*-cut-set. Hence, each column of *C* corresponding to a twig contains _____ (how many?) nonzero element(s). The row containing this nonzero element cannot, therefore, be obtained by linearly combining any of the other rows. Hence, the rows of C are independent.

Now consider the two B matrices so far considered. They are repeated below.

$$B_1 = \begin{bmatrix} -1 & -1 & 0 & 0 & \overbrace{1} & 0 & 0 \\ 0 & 1 & 1 & 0 & 0 & 1 & 0 \\ 0 & 0 & -1 & 1 & 0 & 0 & 1 \end{bmatrix} \quad \text{Links}$$

$$B_2 = \begin{bmatrix} 1 & 0 & 1 & \overbrace{1} & 0 & 0 \\ -1 & -1 & 0 & 0 & 1 & 0 \\ 0 & -1 & 1 & 0 & 0 & 1 \end{bmatrix} \quad \text{Links}$$

By reasoning as for the C matrix, establish whether or not the rows of B are independent.

_____

_____

_____

_____

_____

_____

They are independent.

Each row of B corresponds to an f-loop defined by a link for a selected tree. In the column of B corresponding to this link, there is only one nonzero element and it is in the row of the f-loop defined by that link. Since the elements of the other rows in that same column are zero, no linear combination of the other rows can cause a nonzero element to appear in that column. Hence, no row is dependent on the others. (OES)

28   REVIEW OF LOOPS

If you need confirmation of any answers to the following questions, look back through the last three sections.

Of all the loops in a graph, the *fundamental loops* are the most important. In a graph having b branches and $n + 1$ nodes, there are _____ (how many?) fundamental loops.

Given a tree of a given graph, each fundamental loop contains a single _____ (twig/link).

How is the orientation of an f-loop chosen?

_____

A *planar graph* is one which _____

_____

In a planar graph a mesh is defined as _____

_____

It may or may not be possible to find a tree in a planar graph such that the meshes will be f-loops. It will not be possible if _____

_____

State the scheme by which the elements of the B matrix are determined. _____

_____

_____

Diodes and Diode Networks

1 INTRODUCTION

A diode is a two-terminal electrical device having a nature such that its conducting properties are different in the two possible directions of current flow. One of the most common diodes consists of a semiconductor junction between two types of semiconductor materials, called p type and n type. There are also vacuum and gaseous diodes, in which two electrodes are enclosed in a container which is evacuated or contains a gas at low pressure. Other materials, such as oxide coatings on metal surfaces, exhibit similar properties. In this unit, we are not interested in the physics of diode devices, but rather in the methods of predicting their behavior in circuits of various types.

Specifically, we shall examine typical voltage-current relationships, means for representing them analytically and graphically, and methods for solving for currents and voltages in circuits containing resistors, diodes, and sources which are either constant or varying with time.

2 THE CURRENT-VOLTAGE RELATIONSHIP OF A DIODE (REFERENCE SECTION)

A *diode* is an electronic device having two terminals. Unlike a resistor, the current in a diode is not directly proportional to its voltage. Instead, only a small voltage of one polarity is needed to produce current in one direction, called the *forward direction*; but the same voltage of the opposite polarity produces much less current in the opposite direction, called the *reverse direction.*

The relationship between the current and voltage in a typical diode is shown in Fig. 1, where there is also shown the symbol that will be used to represent the diode. The symbol for a diode includes an arrowhead which, by convention, points in the forward direction. The voltage and current references will always be chosen to form a set of load references, most often as shown in Fig. 1. The diode curve is highly nonlinear. However, in each of the two quadrants in which it appears, we can imagine approximating the curve by a straight line, as shown in Fig. 2. The entire graph here is not linear but it consists of two segments, or pieces, which are straight. So it is appropriately called a *piecewise-linear* approximation of the actual curve.

So long as the voltage and current are positive, the piecewise-linear approximation looks like the graph of a resistor. When the voltage and current are negative, it again looks like a resistor, but a different one, since the slope of the *iv* relationship is different. Sometimes, it is possible to carry this approximation process one step further and to let the slopes of the two lines in the piecewise-linear approximation approach their extreme limits, as shown in Fig. 3.

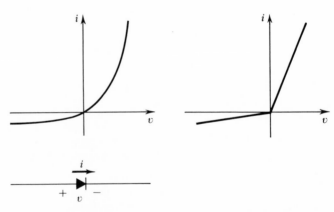

Fig. 1   Diode Curve.   Fig. 2   Piecewise-linear
                                                    Approximation

We shall now invent a hypothetical device called an *ideal diode* whose iv relationship is the one shown in Fig. 3. The

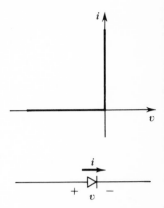

Fig. 3   Ideal Diode.

symbol for an ideal diode is also shown there. To distinguish the ideal from an actual diode, the arrowhead on the diode symbol is left open. The tip of the arrowhead still points in the forward direction. The black arrowhead is a symbol placed on paper to represent a real device. The open arrowhead does not represent a real device, it is a symbol for a model which has the following properties:

(a)   For any value of reverse voltage, the reverse current is zero.

(b)   For any value of forward current, the forward voltage is zero.

3   THE IDEAL DIODE

The graph relating the terminal variables of a diode in the preceding section is a plot of ——————— (v against i/i against v).

For an ideal diode, the value of the slope of the iv graph in the forward direction is ———————; in the reverse direction, the value of the slope equals ———————

For the ideal diode shown below, when $i > 0$, $v =$ ————;
when $v < 0$, $i =$ ————————————

i against v

infinite

zero

0

0

Suppose the voltage across an ideal diode is made to vary. The power absorbed by the ideal diode will equal zero (check one):

(a)   Only when $i > 0$
(b)   Only when $v < 0$
(c)   Always
(d)   Never

State the properties of an ideal diode:

_____

_____

(c)

$i = 0$ when $v < 0$
$v = 0$ when $i > 0$
(or equivalent words)

Using these properties, draw the iv curve of an ideal diode.

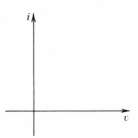

Another way to look at an ideal diode is to compare it with a switch. A switch is either open or closed. The diagram below shows a switch in a network in each of its two positions.

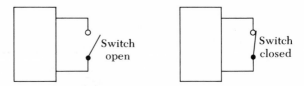

When the switch is open, the current is zero and when the switch is closed the _____ is zero.

voltage

Turning to the diode, when there is a reverse voltage across an ideal diode, it behaves like a(an) _____ (closed/ open) switch. In this case the diode is _____ (conducting/nonconducting); it is equivalent to a(an) _____ (open/short) circuit.

open
nonconducting
open

In the following diagram, the diode _____ (is/is not) ideal. What will be the value of the current, i?

is

Zero

−100

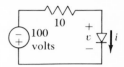

100

closed

short

is

OFF

zero

ON

zero

0

zero

0; 0

True

No

_____. Replace the diode with an equivalent, and redraw the diagram; then determine the value of the diode voltage: $v =$ _____

When there is forward current through an ideal diode, it behaves like a switch that is _____. At such a time it is equivalent to a(an) _____ (open/short) circuit.

A device that must operate in one of two possible conditions is referred to as a *two-state* device, each of the two conditions being one of its states. An ideal diode _____ (is/is not) a two-state device.

The two states of an ideal diode are descriptively called ON and OFF to designate its conducting and nonconducting states, respectively. When there is a reverse voltage across the diode, it is in its _____ state. In the OFF state, the diode current is _____ (zero/positive/negative). When there is forward current, the diode is in its _____ state; the voltage in this case equals _____

For the diode shown below, the power absorbed is given by $p = vi$. When the current is positive, the voltage is

$v =$ _____. Hence, the power in this case equals _____. When the diode voltage v is negative, then $i =$ _____; and $p =$ _____

Is the following statement true or false?

"In either the ON or the OFF state, the power dissipated in an ideal diode equals zero." _____

Is there any situation when the power into an ideal diode is not zero? _____

4   AN IDEAL DIODE IN A NETWORK

When an ideal diode is in a network containing resistors and sources, the first question that must be answered is: What state is the diode in? Once this question is answered, the diode is replaced by the appropriate equivalent circuit, which is either a(an) _____ or a(an) _____. The result is a network containing only resistors and sources, whose solution can be carried out as before.

    In the following diagram, the diode _____ (is/is not) ideal. Its state will be either _____ or _____. To find out which state it is in, let us try assuming it is OFF and observe if this assumption is consistent with the resulting condition in the circuit.

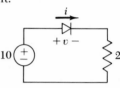

    If the diode is OFF, then $i =$ _____. The voltage across the 2-ohm resistor will then equal _____. Hence, by KVL, the diode voltage $v =$ _____. This _____ (is/is not) consistent with the assumption that the diode is OFF. The conclusion is that the value of i _____ (can/cannot) be zero. What is the state of the diode? _____

    Redraw the diagram with the diode replaced by the appropriate equivalent and solve for i.

    As another simple example, consider the network shown below. To determine the state of the diode, try assuming it is OFF, which means that it will be replaced by a(n) _____ (open/short) circuit.

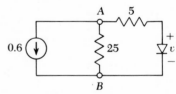

When the diode has been replaced by its equivalent for the OFF state, its voltage v equals _____ (v_{AB}/v_{BA}). The numerical value of v is $v =$ _____. This result _____ (is/is not) consistent with the assumption, and

OFF

so the conclusion is that the diode is in the _____
state.

5 NETWORKS WITH CONSTANT SOURCES

The preceding section gave some illustrations of finding the voltages or currents when an ideal diode is connected in a network containing resistors and constant sources. From these illustrations, we can develop a general procedure. The state of the diode is determined by (a) assuming it to be in one state or the other, and then (b) determining the diode voltage or current from the rest of the network, If this value is consistent with the assumed value, then the diode is in the assumed state. If not, the diode is in the other state.

Thus, suppose the diode is assumed to be OFF. The position occupied by the diode can then be replaced by an open circuit. The resulting (somewhat simplified) circuit can then be solved to determine whether the sign of the diode voltage will be consistent with the assumption. To provide a summary of the possible cases, fill in the following table, indicating whether the assumption is true or false, and whether the diode is ON or OFF:

Assumption: OFF

Sign of diode voltage from trial solution	Assumption is True/False	Diode is ON/OFF
Negative		
Positive		

True; OFF

False; ON

It is also possible to determine the state of a diode by assuming it is ON. A trial solution is then made of a modified circuit in which the diode is replaced by a short circuit, in order to determine the sign of the diode current. Complete the table below for this assumption:

Assumption: ON

Sign of diode current from trial solution	Assumption is True/False	Diode is ON/OFF
Negative		
Positive		

False; OFF

True; ON

In the following diagram, suppose $v_1 = 12$ volts. By making and testing an assumption, it is found that the diode will be _____ (ON/OFF). The currents will have the values

$i_1 = $ _____

$i_2 = $ _____

$i_3 = $ _____

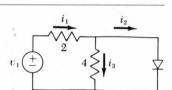

Now suppose $v_1 = -6$ volts. Is the diode ON or OFF? _____. Determine the values of the currents.

$i_1 = $ _____

$i_2 = $ _____

$i_3 = $ _____

In the network below, v_1 and v_2 are constant sources. In a particular case, $v_1 = 30$ volts and $v_2 = 10$ volts. It is required to determine the values of i_1, i_2, and i_3.

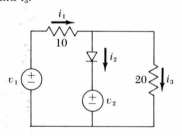

The first step is to determine the state of the diode. Assume it is ON. Then $i_3 = $ _____ amp and $i_1 = $ _____

amp. Then by KCL, $i_2 = $ _____ amp. Is this con-

sistent with the assumption of the state? _____.
Verify your results by assuming the diode is OFF.

The table below refers to the previous circuit. Values of two of the five voltages and currents are given for two different cases. Determine the state of the diode and complete the table by filling in the values of the other three quantities, for each case.

Diode state	v_1	v_2	i_1	i_2	i_3
	volts		amp		
	−5	−20			
	60	50			

ON;   1.5; 2.5; −1

OFF; 2; 0; 2

6 DETERMINING THE SWITCHING CONDITION FOR ONE DIODE

When it is known what state a diode is in (ON or OFF), there is no difficulty in solving for voltages and currents in the remaining network, after the diode is replaced by the appropriate equivalent. The equivalent is either _____

an open circuit

a closed circuit

or _____

In all of the preceding discussion, the only sources in the network were batteries whose voltages were constant. In such a network the diode will (check one):

(a)

(a)   Remain in one specific state

(b)   Switch state from time to time

Now suppose the network includes a source whose voltage is varying with time. In the following network, v_1 is a time-varying voltage. When v_1 is zero, the diode will be _____ (ON/OFF)

OFF

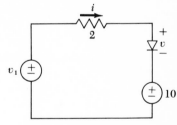

As v_1 varies, its value may from time to time become large enough to cause the diode to switch states. We shall now discuss how to determine the critical values of v_1 at which the switching of states takes place.

0

$v_1 - 10$

Assume the diode is OFF. Then, $i = $ _____, and

$v = $ _____

The assumed condition is true if v is _____ (< 0 or > 0). Thus, the range of values of v_1 for which the diode is ON is: v_1 must be _____ (less than/greater than) 10. In mathematical notation, this is written

v_1 _____

The problem can also be solved by assuming that the diode is ON. The diode current is then given by the expression

$i =$

The assumed condition is true if i is _____ (< 0 or > 0). Does this alternate procedure yield the same range of v_1 for which the diode will be OFF? _____

In this example, the diode *switches* from one state to the other as v_1 passes through the value _____

The pattern followed in this illustration consists of a few simple steps.

(a)   Assume the diode is OFF and write an expression for the diode voltage v in terms of other variables, including the time-varying source variable.

(b)   Set $v < 0$. The expression in (a) gives the range of values of the time-varying variable that will keep the diode OFF, including the critical point at which the state switches.

An alternate procedure is to assume that the diode is ON and to obtain an expression for the diode current i. Then set $i > 0$ to give the range of the time-varying variable for which the diode will be ON.

(*Remark:* It is worthwhile knowing that problems like this can be solved by assuming either that the diode is OFF or it is ON. However, there is often a difference in complexity of the network resulting after the assumption is made. If you can tell ahead of time which is simpler, use the corresponding assumption. Otherwise, choose either assumption.)

As a second illustration consider the diagram below in which i_1 is a time-varying current. When i_1 is zero, the diode in this network will be _____ (ON/OFF)

< 0

less than

$v_1 < 10$

$\dfrac{v_1 - 10}{2}$

> 0

Yes

10

ON

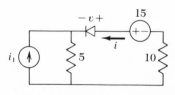

Following the pattern of the steps outlined above, assume the diode is OFF. Then, the diode voltage is given by which of the following:

(d)

   (a) $v = 15 + 5i_1$
   (b) $v = -15 + 5i_1$
   (c) $v = -15 - 5i_1$
   (d) $v = 15 - 5i_1$

3

The switching value of i_1 equals _____, and the diode voltage will be less than zero when i_1 is in the range

> 3

i_1 _____

Repeat the above example, starting with the assumption that the diode is ON.

7 PLOTTING OUTPUT CURVES

In the networks discussed in the preceding section the time-varying source voltage or current can be considered an "input" signal, or an *excitation*. Any one of the resulting currents and voltages in the network can be looked upon as the *response* to this excitation, or the "output." The previous section concentrated on obtaining the switching value of a time-varying source. In this section, we shall discuss two ways of displaying various currents and voltages graphically.

For the first network in the preceding section (repeated below), it was found that

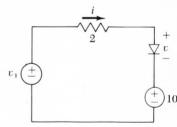

$i = 0$ for $v_1 < 10$

$i = \dfrac{v_1}{2} - 5$ for $v_1 > 10$

A straight line

Each of these expressions describes what kind of curve? _____. On the axes on page 256 sketch the graph of i against v_1 for the range $-5 < v_1 < 25$, labeling the important points where changes occur.

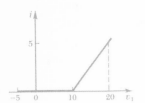

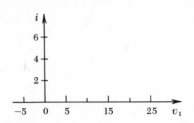

This type of graph, in which an output variable is plotted against an input, is called an *output-input* graph. Besides this, when an input waveshape is given, it is also useful to see the actual variation of the output as a function of time. For the above network, two possible waveshapes of v_1 are plotted below. Plot the waveshape of i for each of the two inputs shown, using the v_1 scale also for i.

(a) $i = 0$ because v_1 never exceeds 10 volts

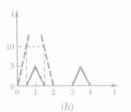

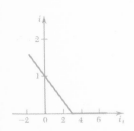

(b)

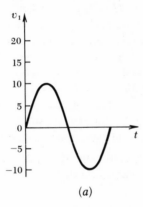

(a)

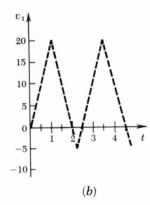

(b)

For the second network in the last section, it is found that

$$i = \begin{cases} 0 & \text{for } i_1 > 3 \\ 1 - \dfrac{1}{3} i_1 & \text{for } i_1 < 3 \end{cases}$$

Plot the output-input graph on the axes given below for the range $-4 < i_1 < 6$.

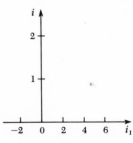

Now suppose that i_1 in this example has, successively, each of the waveshapes plotted in the preceding example for v_1. (The scales for v_1 are now the scales for i_1.) Plot the resulting waveshapes of i on the axes below. Put scales on the axes and show positive and negative peak values.

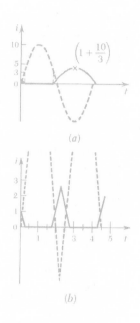

(a)

(b)

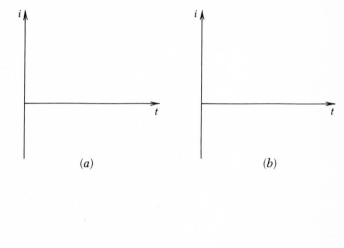

(a)   (b)

8   RECTIFIER AND PEAK DETECTOR

A very important application of diodes is to convert voltages that alternate periodically between positive and negative values to ones that are never negative, or unidirectional. In common (and loose) terminology this process is said to be a conversion from alternating current to direct current.

A simple circuit which accomplishes this function is shown below. For what values of v_1 is the diode conducting? _____.

$v_1 > 0$

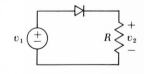

v_1

< 0

0

For the conducting state, $v_2 =$ _____. The diode is not conducting when v_1 _____. In this case,

$v_2 =$ _____

If v_1 has the waveshape shown below in dashed lines, sketch the waveshape of v_2 on the same axes.

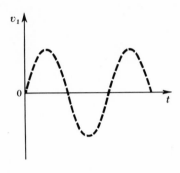

The waveshape of the output is said to be *rectified* and the circuit is called a *rectifier*. For some applications, the above rectifier has the disadvantage that the negative part of the input is suppressed and not utilized in the output. A possible way to fill in the gap is shown in the following diagram. The two sources are identical. (*Remark*: This is a simplified dia-

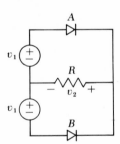

gram. In reality, the effect of two sources is obtained by using a device called a transformer, having two identical secondary windings.)

Specify in the following table whether each diode is ON or OFF when v_1 is positive and when v_1 is negative:

	$v_1 > 0$	$v_1 < 0$
(a) Diode A:	_____	_____
(b) Diode B:	_____	_____

(a)   ON;   OFF
(b)   OFF;   ON

Also, write an expression for v_2 in each of these cases.

(a)   For $v_1 > 0$, $v_2 = $ _____

(b)   For $v_1 < 0$, $v_2 = $ _____

(a) v_1
(b) $-v_1$

Let v_1 have the last waveshape previously shown. Sketch v_2.

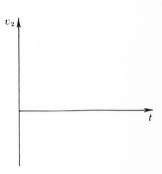

Because both the positive and negative halves of the wave are utilized in the output, this circuit is called a *full-wave* rectifier. What might the previous rectifier be called?

The common name is *half-wave rectifier*

_____

Adding a battery in series with the diode in the half-wave rectifier, as shown below, leads to another application of a diode. In this diagram, when the diode is not conducting, the

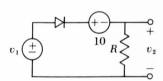

zero

$v_1 < 10$; $v_1 > 10$

$v_1 - 10$

output voltage v_2 equals _____. For what values of v_1 will the diode be OFF? _____. ON? _____. When the diode is ON, $v_2 = $ _____

The preceding can be described by saying that there will be no output until the input exceeds 10 volts. After that, the output equals the input reduced by 10.

If the input waveshape is as shown below, sketch the output voltage v_2 on the same axes.

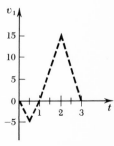

The above is called a *peak-detecting* circuit; it is useful when we are interested in knowing whether or not an input voltage exceeds a certain value.

How would you modify the above diagram if you wanted to detect the presence of peak voltages that exceed 25 volts?

Replace the present battery
with a 25-volt one.

_____

9 VOLTAGE LIMITER

In the operation of certain electrical devices, it is important to ensure that the voltage shall not rise above some specified value. The behavior of a diode as a switch permits such *voltage limiters* to be designed.

The diagram below shows such a network; V_b represents an ideal battery, whose voltage is constant, and v_1 is the *input voltage*, which varies with time. As v_1 varies, the diode will switch state. We must find expressions for the output voltage v_2 when the diode is in each of its states; and we must determine the critical value of v_1 at which the diode switches state.

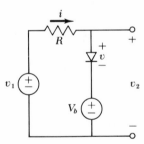

Redraw the diagram for the case when the diode is OFF, replacing the diode by an appropriate equivalent. From this diagram write an expression relating v_2 to v_1.

$v_2 =$ _____ (when diode is OFF)

How would you proceed to establish the values of v_1 for which the diode is OFF?

I would write the expres-
sion for v in terms of v_1 and
set $v_1 < 0$.

_____

_____

Carry out this procedure and determine the range of values of v_1.

$v = v_1 - V_b < 0$

$v_1 < V_b$

The diode will switch state from OFF to ON when

V_b

$v_1 =$ _____

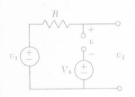

Redraw the diagram for the ON state of the diode and determine the output voltage v_2 for this case.

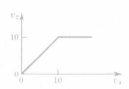

R

v_1 V_b v_2

V_b

$v_1 > V_b$

$v_2 = $ _____ (when diode is ON)

For what range of values of v_1 will the diode be ON? _____

These results are summarized below.

(a) $v_2 = v_1$ for $v_1 < V_b$
(b) $v_2 = V_b$ for $v_1 > V_b$

Let $V_b = 10$ volts and make a plot of the output-input graph below; label the coordinates where the diode switches state.

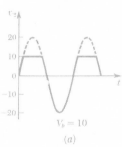

For the same circuit, suppose the input voltage has the waveshape shown below. Sketch the waveshape of v_2 for the two cases:

(a) $V_b = 10$ volts
(b) $V_b = -10$ volts

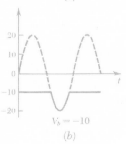

$V_b = 10$

(a)

$V_b = -10$

(b)

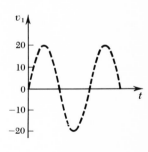

Thus, the combination of a diode and a battery can be used to "limit" the output voltage to values that do not exceed what voltage? _____

The voltage of the battery

10 ANOTHER VOLTAGE LIMITER

In the preceding voltage-limiter network, it was assumed that nothing was connected to the output terminals. More realistically, there is likely to be a load resistance, as represented by R_2 in the following diagram. Everything else is the same as before. Again it is required to find the output voltage v_2 as a function of v_1.

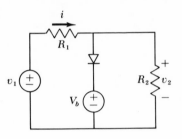

A useful first step is to redraw the diagram twice, once for each state, replacing the diode by an appropriate equivalent. Do this below for each diode state.

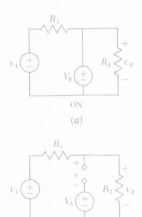

ON

(a)

R_1

OFF

(b)

(a)   ON   (b)   OFF

When the diode is ON, the constant source is directly across the output; and when the diode is OFF, the network is like a voltage divider. The output voltage for the two states can, therefore, be rewritten in terms of v_1 and V_b as

(a) $\dfrac{R_2}{R_1 + R_2}\, v_1$

(b) V_b

(a) $v_2 =$ (diode OFF)

(b) $v_2 =$ (diode ON)

To find the critical value of v_1 at which the diode switches state, we could assume that the diode is OFF, write an expression for the diode _____ (voltage/current) and set it _____. Carry out this procedure and determine the values of v_1 for which the diode is OFF, as well as the critical value at which the diode switches.

voltage
< 0

$v = v_2 - V_b$

$= \dfrac{R_2}{R_1 + R_2}\, v_1 - V_b < 0$

$v_1 < \left(1 + \dfrac{R_1}{R_2}\right) V_b$

Critical value

For concreteness, assume the following values:

$R_1 = R_2$ $V_b = 10$ volts

A summary of the above results is:

(a) $\dfrac{v_1}{2}$;   20

(b) 10;   20

(a) $v_2 =$ _____   for $v_1 <$ _____

(b) $v_2 =$ _____   for $v_1 >$ _____

Make a sketch of the output-input graph, labeling the coordinates of the point at which the diode switches.

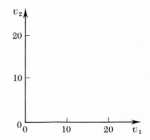

$V_b = 10$ volts

Suppose v_1 rises to 200 volts, the maximum value which the output voltage can take on equals _____

Suppose v_1 has the waveshape shown below. On the same axes, sketch the waveshape of v_2 to scale for two cases (assume $R_1 = R_2$):

(a) $V_b = 10$

(b) $V_b = 0$

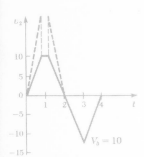

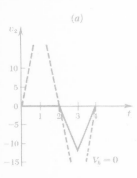

(a)

(b)

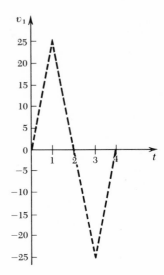

For the numerical values above, the slope of the output-input graph in the OFF state of the diode equals _____

1/2

Suppose the slope is to be increased to make it closer to unity. If R_1 is to be changed to accomplish this, its value should be _____ (increased/decreased).   If R_2 can be changed, it should be _____ (increased/decreased)

decreased

increased

In particular, suppose it is desired to have $v_2 = 0.8v_1$. This can be done by making $R_1/R_2 =$ _____

0.25

11   NEGATIVE AND MULTIPLE LIMITING

The preceding circuits provide limiting of the _____ (positive/negative) excursions of the output voltage.   It is possible also to limit the excursions in the other direction.

positive

OFF

The diode in the following diagram is _____ (ON/OFF) when V_b is positive and v_1 is zero.

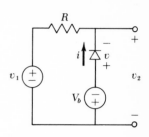

Carry out an analysis to determine expressions for v_2 in terms of v_1 for each of the two states of the diode. Also determine the critical value of v_1.

(a) OFF

(a) Diode OFF

$v_2 = v_1$

$v = -V_b - v_1 < 0$

∴ critical value:

$v_1 = -V_b$

(b) ON

(b) Diode ON:

$v_2 = -V_b$

(also $i = -\dfrac{v + V_b}{R} > 0$,

giving same information)

Plot the output-input graph on the left below, and label the coordinates of the critical point. If v_1 has the waveshape below, plot the waveshape of v_2 on the same axes.

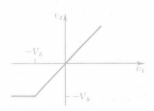

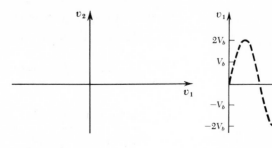

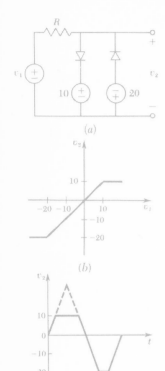

(a)

(b)

(c)

It is possible to combine both positive and negative limiting into a single network.

(a) Design such a network which limits the positive amplitudes to 10 volts and the negative amplitudes to -20 volts (show values). Label the input voltage v_1.

(b) Sketch the output-input graph, labeling critical points.

(c) If v_1 has a symmetrical triangular waveshape whose positive and negative peaks are 30 and -30 volts, respectively, sketch the output voltage waveshape.

12   REVIEW AND APPLICATION PROBLEMS

In networks containing a single diode and a time-varying source, the diode state may switch from time to time. A complete knowledge of the variation of an "output" voltage or current as the input varies can be found by performing a number of steps, which are:

(a) Assume the diode is OFF and find an equation for the output.

(b) find an equation for the output

(b) Assume the diode is ON and _____

(c) Determine the value of the input for which the diode switches state, by either of the following methods:

(i) voltage; < 0

(i) Assume the diode is OFF, obtain an expression for the diode _____ and set it _____

(ii) current; > 0

(ii) Assume the diode is ON, obtain an expression for the diode _____ and set it _____

Note that there is no preferred order in carrying out these steps;
any one may be done first.

Several problems are presented below. In each case, determine expressions for the designated output variable in terms
of the input for both states of the diode; and specify the critical
value of the input. Also make a plot of the output-input graph.

In each case complete the problem, if you can, without
further assistance. If you need help, some suggestions are
given; use them only to the extent you need them.

PROBLEM 1
Consider the input and output in this problem to be, respectively, v_1 and v_2.

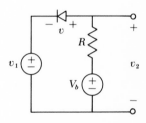

SOLUTION
Write an expression for the diode voltage when the diode is

OFF: $v =$ _____. Since the diode of OFF, this
leads to v_1 _____. Then

$v_2 =$ _____ (diode OFF)

When the diode is ON, $v =$ _____. Hence, in
terms of v_1,

$v_2 =$ _____ (diode ON)

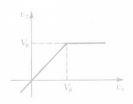

PROBLEM 2

Consider v_1 as the input and v_2 as the output.

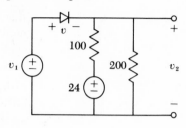

SOLUTION

Write an expression for the diode current when it is ON and set it _____ to find the critical value of v_1.

Then, the output in terms of v_1 will be

$v_2 =$ _____ (diode ON)
$v_2 =$ _____ (diode OFF)

You can also obtain the critical point by assuming the diode is OFF and setting _____ . Do it.

PROBLEM 3

For the circuit shown below, consider the input to be v_1 and the output to be i.

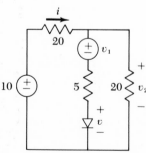

voltage: < 0

$v = -v_1 + v_2$

$\quad = -v_1 + \dfrac{20}{40}(10) < 0$

> 5

$\dfrac{10}{40} = \dfrac{1}{4}$

$\dfrac{5}{12} \quad \dfrac{v_1}{30}$

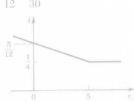

four

(b)

SOLUTION

Assuming the diode is OFF, write an expression for the diode _____ and set it _____ to find the critical value of v_1.

The diode is OFF for v_1 _____. Then,

$i =$ _____ (diode OFF)

When the diode is ON, the two right-hand branches can be replaced by a Thevenin equivalent. Then

$i =$ _____ (diode ON)

13   TWO DIODES IN A NETWORK

When a network contains more than one diode, it is necessary to determine the state of each one. We shall limit our consideration to two diodes only. Each diode will be in one state or the other. There will be a total of _____ possibilities for the combined states.

If all sources in the network are constant, each diode will (check one):

(a)   Switch state from time to time
(b)   Remain in one particular state

A systematic procedure for determining which of the four possible states actually prevails in the network consists of examining the possibilities one at a time.

An illustration is shown in the diagram below. One of the four possible conditions of the diodes is listed in the table, and the corresponding network is shown to the right. Complete this table to show the other possibilities.

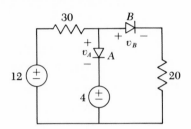

Diode A	Diode B
ON	OFF

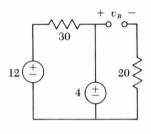

ON;   ON

OFF;   OFF

OFF;   ON

Suppose the first condition listed (*A:* ON, *B:* OFF) prevails. From the corresponding diagram, the voltage across diode *B* is found to be $v_B =$ _____. Is this consistent with the assumption that diode *B* is OFF? _____

4

No

We conclude that the first listed condition (*A:* ON, *B:* OFF) _____ (is/is not) possible.

is not

Next examine the case of both diodes ON. The appropriate diagram is shown below. Suppose each diode current is determined and one or the other is found to be negative. Will this condition be consistent with the assumption of both diodes ON? _____

No

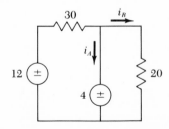

Determine the currents i_A and i_B:

(a) $\dfrac{12-4}{30} - \dfrac{1}{5} = \dfrac{1}{15}$

(a) $i_A =$

(b) $\dfrac{1}{5}$

(b) $i_B =$

Yes

Yes

Are these results consistent with the assumed states? _____

Are both diodes ON? _____

In this example, the second of the four possible states which were examined happened to be the actual state. In order to rule out the remaining two states, is it necessary to examine them in detail? _____. Why or why not?

No

Diode voltages and currents are unique; can't be other than the ones already found.

14 TWO DIODES WITH A TIME-VARYING SOURCE

If all the sources in a network with diodes are constant, each diode will be in one particular state. But if the network contains a time-varying source, then the state of each diode may switch as time goes on. Is it possible in the course of time for the diodes to be in more than one of the four possible combined states? _____

Yes

What is of importance is to determine the value of the input signal at which one or both of the diodes switch state. Again a systematic approach requires examining each of the four possible combined states, to determine the range of values of the input signal for which each of the possible states will prevail. The critical values at which the state is changed occur at the _____ (ends/center) of these ranges.

ends

An illustration is given below. Also shown is a table listing
the possible states. The third column has to be filled in, giving
the range of v_1 for which that state is the correct one. Finally,
the last column is the output voltage for this state.

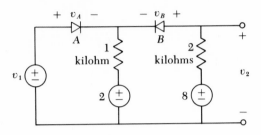

Diode A	Diode B	v_1	v_2
OFF	OFF	Impossible	
OFF	ON		
ON	ON		
ON	OFF		

The first listed state is easily disposed of. When both diodes
are OFF, v_1 _____ (is/is not) connected to the rest of
the network. In this case the sign of v_B is found to be _____
(+/−); this _____ (is/is not) consistent with the assumed state. This state cannot be achieved and is so marked in
the table.

To continue, consider the state (A: OFF, B: ON). (It would
help to redraw the diagram for this state, but the original diagram can be used, if you imagine each diode replaced by its
equivalent.) The current in diode B is $i_B =$ _____
ma. The voltage across diode A can now be written in terms of
v_A and i_B; to be consistent with the assumed state, its range must
be v_A _____. Carry out these steps and obtain a
range of values for v_1.

is not

+

is not

$\dfrac{8-2}{3} = 2$

< 0

$v_A = v_1 - 2 - 1\,(i_B)$

$\therefore\quad = v_1 - 4 < 0$

$v_1 < 4$

$-2i_B + 8 = 4$

The output voltage for this state will be

$v_2 =$ _____ volts

Carry out a similar analysis for the remaining two states and complete the table which is repeated below.

Diode A	Diode B	v_1	v_2
OFF	ON	$v_1 < 4$	4
ON	ON		
ON	OFF		

$4 < v_1 < 8;$ v_1

$v_1 > 8;$ 8

From this information, draw the output-input graph, labeling all critical coordinates.

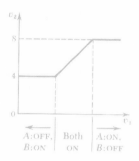

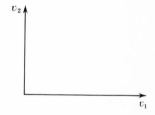

Suppose v_1 has the waveshape shown below, sketch the waveshape of v_2 on the same axes.

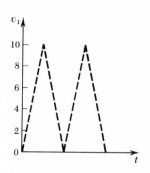

Another network similar to the preceding one is given below. Carry out an analysis similar to the above, arriving at expressions for the output voltage over the entire range of input voltage and clearly indicating the critical points. Also draw an output-input graph. (This problem can serve as a test.)

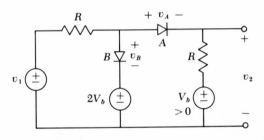

Diode A	Diode B	v_1 (input)	v_2 (output)
OFF	OFF		
OFF	ON		
ON	ON		
ON	OFF		

v_1 (input)	v_2 (output)
$< V_b$	V_b
Impossible	
$> 3V_b$	$2V_b$
$V_b < v_1 < 3V_b$	$(v_1 + V_b)/2$

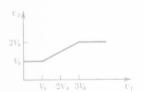

15 LOGIC NETWORKS
In computers and data-processing systems, it is often important to employ circuits which can sense when two or more voltages simultaneously have a prescribed value. Diodes provide a means for accomplishing this.

In the following diagram, v_1 and v_2 may take on the values 0 or 1; V_b is a constant voltage which is much greater than 1 volt. The problem is to determine the value of the output volt-

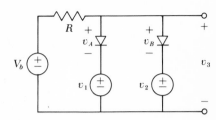

age v_3 under the four possible combinations of the values of v_1 and v_2. As an intermediate step, this will require determining the states of the diodes.

To begin with, let us apply KVL to the loop formed by the two diodes and get

$$v_A = v_B - (v_1 - v_2)$$

When v_1 and v_2 have the same value (both 0 or both 1), $v_A =$ _____. In this case, *if* diode A is ON, then diode B is _____. But *is* diode A ON when $v_1 = v_2$? (You may have to do some work to answer this.) _____. Find the value of v_3 in this case for:

(a) $v_1 = v_2 = 0$ $v_3 =$ _____
(b) $v_1 = v_2 = 1$ $v_3 =$ _____

Now consider the case when $v_1 = 1$ and $v_2 = 0$. Inserting these values above yields $v_A = v_B - 1$. Suppose diode B is ON; then the voltage across diode A will equal _____; so diode A will be _____ (ON/OFF). Is it true that diode B is ON? _____. In this case $v_3 =$ _____

By similar reasoning, the value of v_3 when $v_1 = 0$ and $v_2 = 1$ is found to be $v_3 =$ _____

The preceding results can be summarized in the table below. The first two columns give the four possible combinations of values of v_1 and v_2, and the third column specifies the output voltage. For which values of v_1 and v_2 is the output nonzero?

v_1	v_2	v_3
0	0	0
0	1	0
1	0	0
1	1	1

(margin answers)

v_B
ON
Yes

(a) 0
(b) 1

$-v_1 = -1$
OFF
Yes; 0

0

Both are nonzero, or both equal 1.

This network is called an AND gate. A signal appears at the output when a nonzero signal is present in input 1 AND in input 2.

Is the following true or false? (If false, correct it.)
"In an AND gate it is possible for both diodes to be OFF."

False; *not possible*

[*Remark:* It is worthwhile to note that values 0 and 1 for the input signal are symbolic for logical "no" and "yes"; that is, absence or presence of a signal. In an actual circuit, the values 0 and 10 would be more appropriate, for the practical reason that the greater their difference the easier it is to design a circuit capable of distinguishing between them. Furthermore, it is found that exact values 0 and 1 (or 0 and 10) are not necessary for the operation of the circuit. This is fortunate, because there will always be slight variations of actual voltages from their intended values. (This is the reason for making V_b much greater than 1.) If the circuit is analyzed for the general case of arbitrary values of v_1 and v_2 (less than V_b), it is found that v_3 always equals the minimum of v_1 and v_2. (It is recommended that you prove this.) Thus, in practice 0 might correspond to a signal "less than 1 volt" and 10 to a signal "greater than 9 volts." In that case, if *either* v_1 or v_2 is less than 1, the output will be less than 1; and if v_1 and v_2 are *both* greater than 9, the output will be greater than 9.]

Now suppose the diodes and the battery voltage are both reversed, as shown below. Again V_b greatly exceeds 1 volt; and each of the sources is either 0 or 1 volt. The four possibilities are shown in the table below. By an analysis similar to the above, find v_3 for each case and complete the table

0

1

1

1

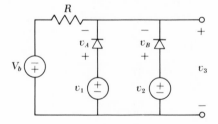

v_1	v_2	v_3
0	0	
0	1	
1	0	
1	1	

In this network, is there a nonzero output voltage v_3 for which values of v_1 and v_2?

Either v_1 or v_2 (or both) are
nonzero or equal 1.

_____

The network is called an OR gate. A signal appears at the output when one OR the other input is nonzero. For what combination of inputs are both diodes OFF? _____

None

(*Remark*: The AND and OR gates are among the simplest of logic circuits. Other circuits which also use diodes can be devised to carry out other operations but the two discussed here are adequate to illustrate the principles.)

16   PIECEWISE-LINEAR APPROXIMATION

Up to this point the diode has been treated as ideal. In the next several sections a model of the diode will be discussed which approximately takes into account the noninfinite slope of the iv curve in the forward direction and the nonzero slope in the reverse direction. This model consists of a combination of resistors and an ideal diode. Modifications introduced by its use in the analysis of diode networks are also discussed.

When this model is used for a diode connected in a network, the resulting network is not different from the ones already discussed, except that a few more resistors are included. No new principles are involved. For this reason, some of you may wish to omit this development and go directly to a discussion of the actual diode itself, starting in Sec. 20.

The current-voltage curve of an ideal diode coincides with the v axis for negative voltage and the i axis for positive current. But an actual diode has an iv curve as shown on the left below.

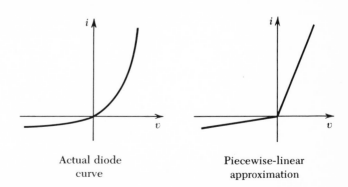

Actual diode
curve

Piecewise-linear
approximation

The piecewise-linear approximation shown on the right is a closer approximation for the actual diode than is the ideal. Specify the quadrants corresponding to the forward and reverse directions.

(a) third

(a) Reverse: _____

(b) first

(b) Forward: _____

In the forward direction, the iv curve for the piecewise-linear approximation is a straight line. Thus, in the forward direction the diode is equivalent to a _____. Let

resistor

the corresponding resistance be called the *forward resistance* R_f. How is R_f related to the iv graph in the first quadrant?

$R_f = \dfrac{1}{\text{slope}};$ zero

_____. For an ideal diode, $R_f = $ _____

In the reverse direction, both an ideal diode and a piecewise-linear diode can be replaced by an equivalent resistance which can be called the *reverse* resistance R_r. From the corresponding iv graph, specify the value of the reverse resistance.

$\dfrac{1}{\text{slope}}$ in third quadrant

Piecewise-linear diode: $R_r = $ _____

R_r

Which is greater, R_f or R_r? _____

Since the actual diode curve is nonlinear, the question of what slope to pick for the piecewise-linear approximation comes up. To be a good approximation, the lines should be drawn as "close" to the actual curve as possible. What it means to be "close" depends upon the range of current or voltage over

piecewise-

which the _____ linear approximation is to be valid. To illustrate, look at the forward portion of an iv curve shown below. Suppose the diode voltage is not expected to exceed

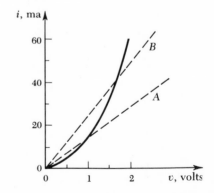

1 volt. Line A might be an adequate approximation. But if the region of interest extends from 0 to 2 volts, line A would not be a good approximation near 2 volts. In this case, line B would yield a better approximation. Find the approximate value of forward resistance represented by each of the two lines.

(a)   Line A: $R_f =$

(a) $\dfrac{2}{30 \times 10^{-3}} = 67$ ohms

(b)   Line B: $R_f =$

(b) $\dfrac{2}{50 \times 10^{-3}} = 40$ ohms

17 PIECEWISE-LINEAR MODEL OF DIODE

The ideal diode has a simple model, or equivalent circuit. It is either a short circuit (ON) or an open circuit (OFF). We shall now discuss a model appropriate for the piecewise-linear approximation.

As a first attempt, consider the parallel connection of a resistor and ideal diode shown below. Sketch the current-voltage curve at the terminals of this network; that is, the graph of i_1 against v_1. Specify the slopes.

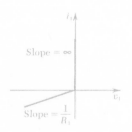

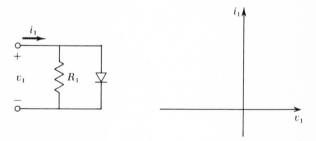

Describe this graph in terms of forward and reverse resistances for the combination:

(a) 0

(b) R_1

(a)   Forward resistance = _____

(b)   Reverse resistance = _____

Draw a modified diagram in which R_1 remains in parallel with the ideal diode, adding a second resistance R_2 such that the forward resistance will not be zero.

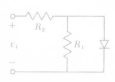

Complete the following:

(a)   The ideal diode is ON when v_1 _____

(b)   The ideal diode is OFF when v_1 _____

(c)   The forward resistance R_f of the network = _____

(d)   The reverse resistance R_r of the network = _____

The diagram below is a model of the piecewise-linear approximation of the diode. Express R_1 and R_2 in terms of R_f and R_r.

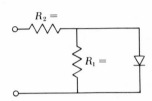

(a) $R_1 = $ _____

(b) $R_2 = $ _____

For a certain diode, suppose that $R_f = 50$ and $R_r = 100{,}000$ ohms. Draw the piecewise-linear model, and specify all resistance values.

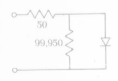

Suppose that R_1 is taken to be equal to R_r in this case. By what percentage will the reverse resistance of the circuit differ from R_r? _____

The preceding values are typical ones for semiconductor diodes. Clearly, an insignificant error is made if the resistance R_1 in the model is replaced by R_r.

While playing around with the piecewise-linear model, a student came up with the idea of moving R_1 to the other side of R_2, as shown below. He thought this might also be a suitable model of the diode. Determine the values R_1 and R_2 in the model, in terms of R_f and R_r.

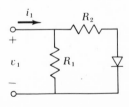

(a) > 0

(b) < 0

(c) R_2

(d) $R_1 + R_2$

(a) $R_r - R_f$

(b) R_f

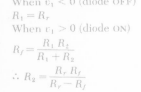

0.05 percent

When $v_1 < 0$ (diode OFF)

$R_1 = R_r$

When $v_1 > 0$ (diode ON)

$$R_f = \frac{R_1 R_2}{R_1 + R_2}$$

$$\therefore R_2 = \frac{R_r R_f}{R_r - R_f}$$

The expression for R_2 can be rewritten as

$$R_2 = R_f \left(\frac{1}{1 - R_f/R_r} \right) \approx R_f \left(1 + \frac{R_f}{R_r} \right)$$

The last step is obtained from the binomial theorem $(1 + x)^n$ $\approx 1 + nx$, when x is much smaller than 1. Suppose R_r and R_f have the numerical values given above. By approximately

0.05 percent

what percentage does R_2 differ from R_f? _____

To summarize, for typical values of forward and reverse resistance each of the networks below can be used as a suitable piecewise-linear approximation of a diode.

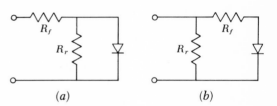

(a)   (b)

For one of these models, the forward resistance is in error, and the reverse resistance is in error for the other. Which is which?

(a)   the reverse

(b)   the forward

(a)   For Fig. (a), _____ resistance is in error
(b)   For Fig. (b), _____ resistance is in error

18 OFFSET VOLTAGE
The actual diode curve shown in the preceding section is repeated below. The previously considered piecewise-linear

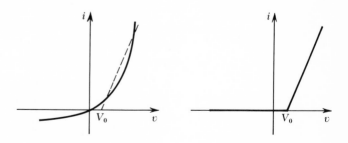

approximation has a break in slope at the origin of the axes. Here instead, an alternative approximation in the forward direction can be made, as illustrated by the dashed line. The break in slope here occurs at a nonzero voltage V_0 called the *offset voltage*. Thus, a possible piecewise-linear approximation is shown in the second diagram, for the particular case in which the value of R_r is assumed to be _____

Draw a network whose iv plot will be the above piecewise-linear curve; it will, therefore, be equivalent to the corresponding diode.

If the reverse resistance is not infinite, this diagram might be modified by adding a resistor in parallel across the terminals, as shown below. Sketch the iv graph for this diagram, using two ranges of the voltage: $v < V_0$ and $v > V_0$. Label the slopes. (Assume that R_r is far greater than R_f.)

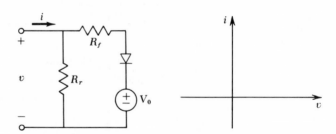

The line in the forward direction does not extend down to the axis at V_0, which is the _____ voltage.

A piecewise-linear approximation of a certain diode is found to have an offset voltage of 1 volt, a forward resistance of 100 ohms, and a reverse resistance of 100 kilohms. Draw a model of the diode and put numerical values on all the components.

19 A VOLTAGE LIMITER WITH A NONIDEAL DIODE

In preceding sections, the ideal diode was found to be useful in a variety of applications, including voltage limiters. The piecewise-linear model can be used in these applications. However, there will now be some differences which we shall investigate here. (This section can be omitted without affecting continuity.)

A simple voltage limiter is shown in the diagram below, where V_b represents the constant voltage of a battery and v_1 varies with time. Judging from its symbol, the diode here

is not _____ (is/is not) ideal.

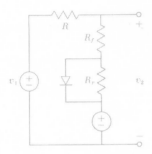

(one possible equivalent)

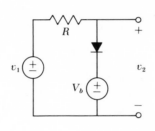

Assume a zero offset voltage and replace the diode with a piecewise-linear equivalent circuit. Redraw the diagram. The problem is to obtain the output-input graph (curve of v_2 versus v_1). It is necessary to find the following three things:

(a) v_2 as a function of v_1 when the ideal diode is OFF

(b) v_2 when the diode is ON

(b) _____

_____

(c) The critical value of v_1 when the diode switches

(c) _____

_____

From the expression for the ideal diode voltage, the value of v_1 at which the diode switches state is:

V_b

$v_1 =$ _____

Determine expressions for v_2 in the two ranges. (Use the approximation $R_f + R_r \approx R_r$.)

(a) $v_2 = \dfrac{R_r v_1}{R + R_r} + \dfrac{RV_b}{R + R_r}$

(a) For $v_1 < V_b$, $v_2 =$

(b) $v_2 = \dfrac{R_f v_1}{R + R_f} + \dfrac{RV_b}{R + R_f}$

(b) For $v_1 > V_b$, $v_2 =$

A sketch of the v_2v_1 graph is shown below.

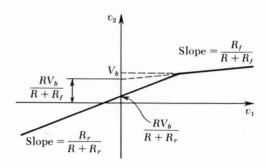

If $R_f = 100$ and $R_r = 100$ kilohms, the preceding expressions become:

For $v_1 < V_b$:

$$v_2 = \frac{1}{1 + \dfrac{R}{100,000}}\, v_1 + \frac{V_b}{1 + \dfrac{100,000}{R}}$$

For $v_1 > V_b$:

$$v_2 = \frac{1}{1 + \dfrac{R}{100}}\, v_1 + \frac{V_b}{1 + \dfrac{100}{R}}$$

In both regions, the graph of v_2 against v_1 is a straight line with a nonzero slope. For comparison, write the slopes for the above limiter and also for one employing an ideal diode.

	Slope for	
	$v_1 < V_b$	$v_1 > V_b$
(a) Ideal diode:		
(b) Nonideal diode:		

(a) 1;   0

(b) $\dfrac{1}{1 + \dfrac{R}{100,000}}$; $\dfrac{1}{1 + \dfrac{R}{100}}$

Also, write the values of the intercepts of each line on the vertical axis (extended line, if necessary).

	Vertical intercept for	
	$v_1 < V_b$	$v_1 > V_b$
(a) Ideal:		
(b) Nonideal:		

Left-margin answers:

(a) $0;\quad V_b$

(b) $\dfrac{V_b}{1+\dfrac{100,000}{R}}\;;\quad \dfrac{V_b}{1+\dfrac{100}{R}}$

$\dfrac{1}{1+\dfrac{R}{100,000}}$

$\dfrac{V_b}{1+\dfrac{100}{R}}$

(a) 1

(b) 1

0

∞

$\dfrac{R}{100,000}=\dfrac{100}{R}$

$R=\sqrt{100(100,000)}$
$=1,000\sqrt{10}$

$\sqrt{R_f R_r}$

For the nonideal case, focus attention on the slope when $v_1 < V_b$ (it equals _____), and on the vertical intercept when $v_1 > V_b$ (it equals _____). For each of these to take on its ideal value would require

(a) $1+\dfrac{R}{100,000}=$ _____

(b) $1+\dfrac{100}{R}=$ _____

To satisfy the first of these requires $R =$ _____.
To satisfy the second one requires $R =$ _____.
Clearly, these are incompatible. A compromise is the best we can do. A possible compromise might be to require that each expression differ from unity by the same amount. Impose this condition and find a value of R.

This expression, in fact, gives a general design formula for choosing the value of R in the limiter network, on the assumption of the stated compromise. For any (nonideal) values of R_f and R_r, the resistance R is chosen to be $R =$ _____

To summarize, the preceding general formulas are collected here.

$$v_2 = \frac{R_r}{R+R_r}\,v_1 + \frac{R}{R+R_r}\,V_b \qquad v_1 < V_b$$

$$v_2 = \frac{R_f}{R+R_f}\,v_1 + \frac{R}{R+R_f}\,V_b \qquad v_1 > V_b$$

$$R = \sqrt{R_f R_r}$$

Assume a specific example of voltage limiter, where $R_f = 400$ and $R_r = 90,000$ ohms. The input is a triangular voltage wave with a peak value of 10 volts. The battery has a voltage of 5 volts. Find the maximum value of the output voltage.

Choose $R = \sqrt{400\ (90,000)}$

$= 6,000$

Peak v_2 occurs when v_1 is maximum.

Peak $v_2 = \dfrac{400}{6,400}\ (10)$

$+ \dfrac{6,000}{6,400}\ (5)$

$= 5.31$ volts

By what percentage does it differ from the maximum value of the output if the diode is taken to be ideal?

Percentage $= \dfrac{(5.31 - 5)}{5}\ 100$

$= 6.2$ percent

20   THE ACTUAL DIODE (REMARK)

Up until now, we have represented an actual diode by simplified models: the *ideal model* and the *piecewise-linear model*. In the case of each of these two models, only some of the features of the real diode are accurately represented. The simplest model (the ideal diode) takes into account only the switchlike character of the actual diode. The piecewise-linear model constitutes a further refinement and includes the approximate effects of a small nonzero forward voltage and a small nonzero reverse current. These models are very useful but neither one provides an exact representation of an actual diode. Thus, results obtained with their use are necessarily approximate, although the approximation may be adequate in many applications.

Because the actual diode iv curve is not linear, the methods previously described are sometimes not sufficiently accurate. Determination of the exact solution of the nonlinear problem represented by an actual diode in a network of resistors and sources requires a new attack, to which we shall turn our attention during the remainder of this unit.

21 SIMULTANEOUS SOLUTION OF A LINEAR AND A NONLINEAR EXPRESSION

The basic circuit we shall deal with is shown below. The

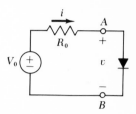

symbol for the diode shows that this diode is _____

actual

(ideal/actual). The source is an ideal battery having a constant voltage V_0.

The iv relationship of the diode is sketched below. This is a

nonlinear

_____ (linear/nonlinear) curve. Suppose the value

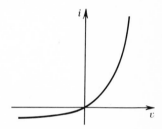

of current i is known. Is it possible to find the diode voltage

Yes

v from the curve? _____

From a consideration of the circuit to the *left* of terminals AB in the above diagram, write an expression relating i to v.

$$\frac{V_0}{R_0} - \frac{1}{R_0} v$$

$i =$

straight line

This equation represents a _____ (what kind of line?). On the axes shown below, sketch the graph of this equation, labeling the slope and both intercepts.

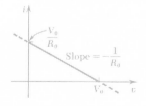

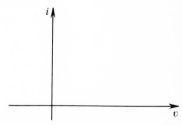

negative

The slope is _____ (positive/negative)

Is the i in the equation of this line the same as the diode

current? _____. There are now two relationships
for i in terms of v. Are there equations for both relationships?

_____. Are there graphs for both relationships?
_____. Suggest how the two relationships can be
solved simultaneously to find the solution for i. _____
_____
_____

Thus, although we do not have an algebraically obtained
solution, we have a graphical one. The diagram below shows a
simultaneous plot of the diode curve and the straight line.
The straight line has intercepts on the axes as follows:

(a) i intercept = _____

(b) v intercept = _____

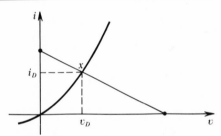

Because the resistor in the circuit is often a "load," the
straight line is called the *load line*. The intersection of the
curve and the load line is marked x on the graph. Reading from
the diagram, the value of current which will flow through the

diode equals _____. The voltage across the diode
_____ (is/is not) equal to the voltage determined
by the intersection of the curve and the load line.

The diode in the diagram below has the iv curve shown.
Determine the diode voltage and the power dissipated in the
resistor; specify the units of measure.

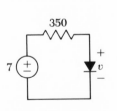

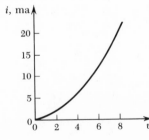

(a) ≈ 4.5 volts

(b) ≈ 17 milliwatts
     (since $i ≈ 7$ ma)

(a) $v =$ _____

(b) $p_R =$ _____

(Go to the next section if you omitted Secs. 16–19.)

Suppose we were to represent the diode by a piecewise-linear approximation having an offset voltage of 0 and a forward resistance of R_f. Find the value of R_f which would yield the same current in the diode.

With diode replaced by R_f:

$$\frac{7}{350 + R_f} = 0.007; \; R_f = 650$$

22   THE LOAD LINE

In a circuit containing an actual diode in series with a battery and a resistor, the diode current and voltage are found in the following way:

On the same axes as the iv curve of the diode, we draw the

load line

_____.   The diode current and voltage are read

Intersection

from the graph at what point of the two curves? _____

two

In order to draw a load line, it is necessary to know _____ (how many?) points. In the preceding circuit, suppose the battery voltage is 10 volts and the resistance is 2 kilohms. Two convenient points for drawing the load line have the following coordinates.

	v coordinate, volts	i coordinate, ma
(a) 10; 0	(a) Point 1: _____	_____
(b) 0; 5	(b) Point 2: _____	_____

Suppose that R_0 and V_0 are limited to the ranges given below. Shade that portion of the iv plane which is the locus of all load lines satisfying these conditions.

1 kilohm $< R_0 <$ 2 kilohms

$10 < V_0 < 50$

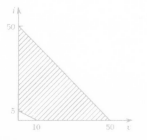

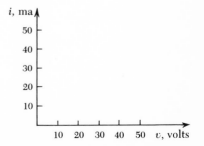

The iv curve of the diode in the diagram below is the one shown.

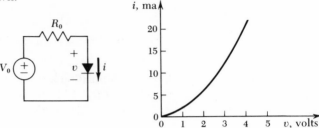

(a) Suppose $V_0 = 4$ volts and $R_0 = 250$ ohms. Find the diode current and voltage (include units of measure).

(a) (i) 7.5 ma

(ii) 2.2 volts

    (i) $i =$ _____

    (ii) $v =$ _____

(b) Suppose $V_0 = 5$ volts and it is desired that the diode voltage be 2 volts. The job is to find the value of R_0. This can be done in two ways that are essentially equivalent.

    (i) By projecting a line up from the v axis, the point on the diode curve corresponding to $v = 2$ volts can be marked. From the curve, the diode current is read

6

        to be approximately _____ ma. The equation of the load line in general literal notation

$\dfrac{V_0 - v}{R_0}$

        (with letters) is $i =$ _____. Using numerical values in this equation, the value of R_0 is calculated as

$\dfrac{5-2}{6 \times 10^{-3}}$

or approx. 500 ohms

        $R_0 =$

    (ii) An alternative is to draw the load line through the intercept on the v axis and the point on the diode curve corresponding to $v = 2$. Let the intercept on the i axis be labeled I_0. Then an expression for R_0 in literal form is

$\dfrac{V_0}{I_0}$

        $R_0 =$

        Find the numerical value of I_0 and verify the value of R_0 previously found.

From load line:

$I_0 \approx 10$ ma

$R_0 = \dfrac{5}{10 \times 10^{-3}}$

$= 500$ ohms

        $R_0 =$

(c)   Suppose $V_0 = 5$ volts and it is desired that the diode current shall be 10 ma. Find R_0.

(c)   From load line:
$I_0 \approx 21$ ma
$c \approx 2.6$ volts
$R_0 \approx 240$ ohms

$R_0 =$

(d)   With $R_0 = 400$ ohms, it is desired that the diode current shall be 7.5 ma. Find the required value of V_0.

(d)   From curve:
$v \approx 2.2$ when $i = 7.5$.
$V_0 = v + R_0 i \approx 5.2$ volts

$V_0 =$

23   MORE EXTENSIVE NETWORKS

In the discussion of the last two sections on the actual diode, the only network considered was a series circuit of a single diode, a single resistor, and a single voltage source. This is not as restrictive as it appears. Let us continue limiting ourselves to a single diode but let it be embedded in an extensive network of resistors and sources.

An illustration is the network below. Viewed from the terminals of the diode, the rest of the network can be replaced by an equivalent, as shown, called the _____ equivalent.

Thevenin

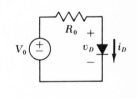

From the diagram, numerical values of V_0 and R_0 are found to be:

(a)   2

(b)   50

(a) $V_0 =$ _____ volts

(b) $R_0 =$ _____ ohms

If the diode is specified, as far as the equivalent circuit is concerned, you now know how to find the diode current i_D and diode voltage v_D. But suppose our interest is in the current i_1 in the 60-ohm resistor in the original diagram rather than in i_D. Can it be determined from the original diagram by using the already determined values of i_D and v_D? _____

Yes

i_D

$26i_D + v_D$

Thus, the current in the 26-ohm resistor equals _____.
Then, in terms of i_D and v_D, the voltage $v_{AB} = $ _____.
From this, the current in the 40-ohm resistor can be found.
Finally, KCL yields i_1. Write an expression for i_1 in terms of
v_D and I_D.

$i_D + \dfrac{26i_D + v_D}{40}$

or

$\dfrac{5 - 26i_D - v_D}{60}$

$i_1 = $

Thevenin
load

In summary, when a single diode is embedded in a network
of resistors and sources, this network as viewed from the terminals of the diode can be replaced by a _____
equivalent. By drawing a _____ line on the same
axes as the diode curve, the diode current and voltage are
found. These values are then used in the original network to
determine the voltage or current of any other branch.

Two networks are shown below. In each case draw a network from which the diode voltage and current can be found
and give numerical values for all components of the equivalent
networks.

Diagram same as
immediately preceding
one (Thevenin equivalent).
$V_0 = 20$ $R_0 = 14.6$

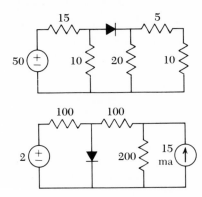

$V_0 = 2.25$ $R_0 = 75$

The curve of the diode in the network below is as shown.
Find the power delivered by the 120-volt battery.

Thevenin values are:
$V_0 = 20$
$R_0 = 25$

From load line:

$v_D = 13$ $i_D = 0.25$

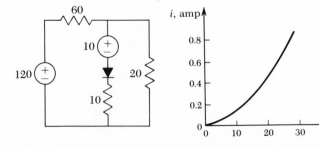

Voltage across 20 ohms
$= 10 + c_D + 10 i_D = 25.5$

i in 60 ohms $= \dfrac{120 - 25.5}{60}$

$= 1.58$

Power $= 120(1.58)$

$= 190$ watts

24   POWER DISSIPATION IN DIODE

Up to this point a very important and practical feature of the
diode has not been considered; this is its power dissipation
capability. The dissipation of power in any electrical device
results in the generation of heat and, thus, a rise in temperature.
Any given electrical device will operate properly only when
its temperature does not exceed a certain limit. This makes it
necessary to place an upper limit on the power dissipated in
the device. This limit is called the *maximum power rating*.
Real diodes will have such ratings. A diode will operate properly only when the power dissipated in it does not exceed

maximum power rating

Yes

its_____. Does the maximum power rating depend on the amount of cooling provided? _____

For a load set of voltage and current references, the power
dissipated in the diode is

vi

$p =$ _____

In the last problem of the preceding section, find the value
of the power dissipated in the diode.

$13(0.25)= 3.25$

$p =$ _____ watts

Assuming forward voltage and current references, the power
dissipated in a diode is $p = vi$. Placing an upper limit on the
product of v and i is equivalent to restricting the range of the
diode curve over which the diode is permitted to operate. The
nature of this restriction is conveniently displayed by plotting
the relationship between i and v that arises when the power
is at the maximum rating.

Suppose the maximum power rating of a diode is P_m watts.
Write an expression involving v and i which expresses this

$vi \leqq P_m$

limitation. _____

The boundary of the region in the iv plane defined by this
limitation is obtained by replacing the inequality by an equals
sign. When this is solved explicitly for i, it becomes $i = P_m/v$.

A hyperbola

What kind of curve is represented by the equation? _____

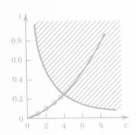

A diode curve is given below. The maximum power rating

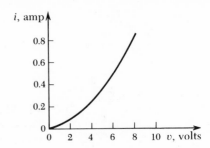

of the diode is $P_m = 1$ watt. Draw directly on the same axes the maximum power curve; place a set of circles (like this: ⊶⊶⊶) on the portion of the diode curve that may be used without danger of damaging the diode; crosshatch the region of the iv plane in which the diode must not operate.

Suppose the diode represented by the preceding curve is in series with a resistor $R_0 = 12.5$ ohms and a voltage source of 10 volts. The power dissipated in the diode _____ (will/will not) exceed the maximum power rating.

Suppose the voltage of the source can be varied while keeping R_0 the same. In your own words, describe two ways to find the maximum value this voltage can have without causing excessive power dissipation in the diode. Then find this value. The curves are redrawn on the next page for convenience.

(a) Graphical: _____

_____

_____

_____

will

(a)

With R_0 unchanged, the slope of the load line remains the same. Move the previous load line parallel to itself to intersect the diode curve and P_m curve at their intersection. (OES)

(b)

$$i_m = \frac{V_0 - v_m}{R_0}$$

$V_0 = v_m + R_0 i_m$

From the graph:

$V_0 = 4 + 12.5(0.25)$

$\quad = 7.1$ volts

(b) Algebraic (in terms of coordinates v_m and i_m of point where diode curve and P_m curve intersect):

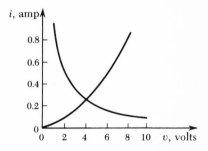

Now suppose the source voltage is limited to 5 volts but R_0 can be changed. Find the minimum value of R_0 necessary to prevent excessive power dissipation in the diode.

The load line must pass through the point (5,0) and the intersection of the diode and P_m curves whose coordinates were previously found to be (4,0.25)

$v = 5 - R_0 i$

$4 = 5 - (0.25)R_0$

$R_0 = 4$ ohms

$R_0 =$

INDEX

INDEX